Other Aladdin Books by
August Derleth

THE CAPTIVE ISLAND
THE COUNTRY OF THE HAWK
EMPIRE OF FUR
LAND OF GRAY GOLD

Land of
Sky-Blue Waters

Land of
Sky-Blue Waters

by AUGUST DERLETH

Illustrated by Frank Hubbard

ALADDIN BOOKS
New York: 1955

LIBRARY OF CONGRESS CATALOG CARD NUMBER: 55-6508

ALADDIN BOOKS IS A DIVISION OF AMERICAN BOOK COMPANY
COPYRIGHT, 1955, BY AUGUST DERLETH. All rights reserved.
No part of this book protected by the above copyright may
be reproduced in any form without written permission of
the publisher.   FIRST EDITION

PRINTED IN THE UNITED STATES OF AMERICA

Contents

Land of
Sky-Blue Waters

Detroit

IT WAS ALMOST MIDNIGHT of a May day in 1820.

Despite the lateness of the hour, young Henry Schoolcraft sat writing in his journal, where he kept a record of
his first trip from New York to the Territory of Michigan. He was on board ship, the *Walk-in-the-Water*, a
steamboat which plied the Great Lakes.

He was a young man of medium height, thin rather
than stocky, but no less sturdy for all that. He was muscular, and filled with quick, ready energy. His blue eyes
never wavered as he read over what he had written.

3

The door of the cabin burst open suddenly. "We're coming in to Detroit, Henry!"

Alex Chase stood there, beckoning him impatiently. Unlike Henry, who was in his twenties, Alex was still in his teens.

"Get your things together, Henry. Captain Rodgers said we disembark just as soon as we touch land."

"But it's midnight!" protested Henry.

"Detroit's all hustle and bustle. They don't waste six hours waiting for the sun to rise before they do things," answered Alex, laughing. "Come on."

The third of the three young men who had traveled together all the way from New York was already on deck. Captain David Douglass was trying to look through the midnight darkness.

The first thing Henry noticed when he came up to David and Alex was that the ship was no longer on Lake Erie. They were now traveling up a river.

"It's the Detroit River," explained David. "You were so busy writing, you never noticed when we left the lake. See, over there's Detroit. The torches are burning at the fort."

"Why, it's almost a city!" exclaimed Henry.

Alex laughed. "I guess we all thought we'd find just a cluster of wigwams around a fort. The way those lights are spread out, there must be more than a hundred houses there."

By now, the steamboat was preparing to come into the harbor. Men were shouting to the shore from the ship, and others on shore were shouting back.

Henry could see for himself, by the light of many lanterns along the shore, that he was not coming into the raw Western settlement he had imagined Detroit to be. Houses rose ghost-like in the background. They were dwellings, shops, even warehouses.

The light of lanterns danced along the street; they were in the hands of a group of people coming down toward the shore. All along the shore of the harbor lanterns stood at regular intervals to light the work of the roustabouts who were there to help the ship dock and to unload it.

Captain Rodgers' voice could be heard above all others. He was shouting orders just as fast as he could think of them. There was as much bustle on board ship as there was on shore. Everyone seemed to be running every which way. Yet, in a few moments, the ship's movement stopped and the bustle tempered down. Now each man had his work to do, and he went at it.

Captain Rodgers still kept shouting orders, but he was less urgent now. In a little while, his voice sounded quite close by. Then he himself loomed up suddenly out of the darkness. He was a fat, jolly man, but his black beard made him look surprisingly fierce.

"My compliments, Gentlemen," he said, spying the

three of them. "We've reached Detroit. If you're ready, you may leave ship to suit your pleasure. Though I'd say now's the time, because, if my ears don't lie to me, you're being waited on."

Even as Captain Rodgers spoke, all could hear a loud voice rising above the din on shore. It seemed to come from a man at the head of the little procession which they had seen bearing down the street toward the river's edge.

"Make way for the Governor! Make way for the Governor!"

Other voices took up the cry and echoed it, and the workers on shore stood aside to allow the party to come through.

"Do you suppose the Governor himself has come to meet us?" asked Alex.

"He seems to want us on his expedition," said David. "Why not?"

"We'll go and see," said Henry.

"I'll send your luggage around, Gentlemen," promised Captain Rodgers. "We'll lie in for a few hours tomorrow."

They bade the Captain good-by and walked off the ship.

Five men stood just a little way from the landing place. No less than three of them were military men, two with the rank of Major, one a General! The man holding the lantern wore the uniform of a lieutenant. He was calling out now—"Mr. Schoolcraft! Mr. Chase! Captain Douglass! This way, please!"

The man in the middle of the group was unmistakably the one in authority. He was a heavy man, with a large and impressive head. When he smiled, his jowls creased on both sides of his mouth. And when he laughed, as he did now at sight of the three coming his way, his whole body seemed to shake.

"Governor Lewis Cass—at your service, Gentlemen," he said. "You'll pardon me—I'm a-quiver with the ague. I'll say no more than bid you welcome, and tell you Major Biddle will see you to your lodgings. No doubt you'll need a good night's rest. I'll hope to see you at my office between ten and twelve in the morning. And I'll expect you to dine with me tomorrow."

He shook hands gravely with all three of them. He said a few words to each of them. But it was before Henry that he paused the longest, holding Henry's hand in his.

"Mr. Schoolcraft, I am happily surprised to find so young-looking a man instead of the grave geologist I expected. I had the pleasure of reading your fine book on the lead mines of Missouri, and I was delighted when the Secretary of War recommended you for our little expedition."

"Thank you, sir."

"I shall hope to see you promptly at ten tomorrow, Mr. Schoolcraft."

Thereupon, the Governor and his party walked away. They left behind only Major John Biddle, who stood with the lantern in his hand, ready to show the three travelers where they were to lodge until the journey into the Northwest began.

In the morning Henry rose before the others. He did not think of breakfast. He was too eager to get outside his lodginghouse, to see what the city of Detroit looked like by daylight. Besides, he needed to find the public armorer and order some geologists' hammers made for him. These were small, handy tools he used to split open stones and rocks, for Henry was a student of stones and ground formations. He had brought none of these hammers with him, since he had been told someone here could make them for him. Wherever it was they were going, it was certain that the hammers would be needed, and Henry had to be sure there would be enough time to get them ready.

Leaving Alex Chase and Captain Douglass still lying asleep, he went out into the morning sun. There he stood in the midde of the street and looked around him. His lodginghouse was on a little rise. From the doorway he could see that Detroit stood on the west bank of the strait which connected the Detroit River to little Lake

St. Clair. He knew that this lake in turn led to the River St. Clair and north into Lake Huron.

Houses rose on every side. There were as many as two hundred, maybe three, Henry guessed. Detroit must have fifteen hundred inhabitants at least, not counting the garrison of soldiers in the fort.

Henry asked the first man he saw where he could find the public armorer's shop. He had to ask two more people, before he received directions. Then he set out for the shop.

He found the public armorer already at work. His shop door stood open, and he could be seen just inside the door, working at a heavy table. He was a white-haired man of middle age. He looked around when Henry's step fell to his ear.

"Good morning, sir!" he boomed in a jolly voice. "At your service, sir!"

Henry introduced himself and told the armorer just what he wanted. He went into precise detail.

The armorer listened to his descriptions without a word. For a few moments Henry wondered whether the older man understood.

"And how soon would the gentleman want the hammers?" asked the armorer.

"Can you make them, sir?"

"I can make them—in three days."

"I'll call for them three days hence," promised Henry.

When he left the armorer's shop, Henry set out in the direction of the harbor because he wanted to find out something about the wilderness to the northwest, which was the direction the expedition was to travel.

As he walked along, Henry was puzzled to see that most of the buildings in Detroit were new. But every now and then he saw charred walls, and he guessed at last that the older town had been destroyed by fire. That would explain why, in this newer Detroit, the streets were much wider than those in New York or Buffalo. The buildings were mostly painted wood though there were several of brick or stone. The city looked much neater than many towns in the East, though pigs and ducks made themselves comfortable in the lanes and side streets.

Everywhere in the streets people were in as much of a hurry as they had been on ship and shore last midnight. But nowhere was there as much running to and fro as at the harbor. It seemed as if ships, long canoes, flatboats, and smaller craft were standing in line waiting to come to shore. They were moving in and out all the time. The shore was crowded with people. There were shippers bringing merchandise in from the East, passengers for the West coming off the boats, and those returning to the East going on board. Voyageurs from the lake country were hauling furs up into town, soldiers and Indians mov-

ing in and out. Henry saw the *Walk-in-the-Water* being re-loaded and taking on passengers for the return trip to Buffalo.

As he stood near the water's edge, Henry saw a large canoe, paddled by two Indians and a voyageur, come in. The voyageur was roughly but warmly clad. He wore clothes which were colorful, in contrast to Henry's own dark suit. His canoe was brightly decorated in red and yellow colors. It was piled high with animal skins. The two Indians were naked to the waist, except for beaded bands about their heads. Their skin shone bronze in the morning sun.

The voyageur sprang to shore almost at Henry's feet.

"In from the North?" Henry asked.

The voyageur looked him up and down. Then he nodded curtly. It was plain that he thought Henry was in the way. But Henry did not move.

"Where from?" he asked.

"By gar! you ask many questions," said the voyageur impatiently.

"I ask because I want to know. I came in last night from the East. I'm bound for the Northwest Passage. I want to know what it's like."

"Ha!" snorted the voyageur with a grin. "You find out. Trees—waters—Indians!"

Henry smiled. "So I begin to find out," he said.

"Ha! But I do not come all the way. Only halfway to Michilimackinac. Else I would have brought my furs to Michilimackinac, not to Detroit."

Under Henry's friendly persistence, the voyageur thawed and became more amiable. Bit by bit, Henry drew the man out. While he had not come from far away this time, before this he had gone far up the course that Governor Cass's expedition would take. Indeed, he had gone farther—beyond the straits of Michilimackinac, past the Sault de Ste. Marie, on to the far end of Lake Superior, which lay above the Territory of Michigan. He had gone as far into the West as the Lake of the Woods, and would have gone farther, had not the cold come and forced him back before he was frozen into the wilderness. Few lived to tell about being caught in the time of snow and ice.

"The cold—you watch heem," said the voyageur. "Come by night—an' then, pouf! you are lost!"

"And the Indians? How are they?"

The voyageur shrugged and raised his eyes heavenward. There were so many Indians, he explained. There were great encampments where the Indians belonging to the same nation, met. There were many small Indian villages. As a traveler moved north, the first Indians he met were the Hurons and Saginaws. Then, for most of the way west, there were the Chippewas, many villages of them. Farther west, past the land of the Chippewas, there were the Winnebagos and the Sioux. All were friendly, except maybe some of the Sioux.

"But me, by gar! I say you no can tell about the red men," said the voyageur. "They are strange people—vair' strange. One time they own all this land—right here— this place, Detroit, one time it was Indian village. But if you go nort'—you see all this yourself. Pairhaps more— if you leave the canoe and go inland."

As he listened, Henry could see in his imagination the majestic woods of the wilderness country. He could picture the wild blue waters of lakes and streams. He could imagine the strange red brother to the white man—the wilderness Indian. Would that Indian be like to those who walked here among the citizens of Detroit? As he listened, his pulse quickened with excitement and the hope that the journey would soon begin.

But now the voyageur waved him off. He had said more than he meant to say. There was much work for him to do.

Henry thanked him and moved away. Judging by the position of the sun, the hour was approaching ten. Governor Cass had asked to see him promptly at ten.

He found someone to direct him to the building where Governor Cass could be found, and walked rapidly toward it, with eager, confident strides.

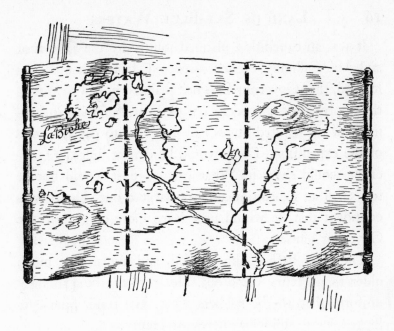

The Birch-Bark Map

ONCE HE STOOD in the anteroom of Hull House, the
Governor's brick residence, Henry was less sure of himself. He knew that his long journey from New York to
Detroit had not left him looking his best. His brief meeting with Governor Cass the night before had not told
him what kind of man the Governor might be. All he
had to go by was the assurance of Mr. Calhoun, the Secretary of War, that he would be treated fairly if he chose
to go on a journey into the wilderness as the geologist of
the party.

It was an expedition planned jointly by the Governor and Mr. Calhoun. Henry suspected, from what he had learned, that Governor Cass had planned it, and then won the approval of the Secretary of War, for the Government of the United States had promised to pay the costs of the expedition. There would be danger, but the Governor would share it. What was more, it would not be too small an expedition nor too large a one. Henry was confident that he would now learn more of it from the Governor himself.

The door before him opened, and a man not much older than Henry came out. He wore the blue military uniform that all the soldiers wore. His frank blue eyes looked with unhidden interest at Henry.

"Mr. Schoolcraft?"

"Yes, sir."

The military man held out his hand. "I am Major Robert Forsyth, the Governor's secretary. The Governor would like to see you now."

He turned without saying anything more and led the way into a plain, simply-furnished room. The same man who had greeted the travelers so curtly at midnight sat there at a table covered with maps and documents. He smiled pleasantly as he stood up when Henry and Major Forsyth entered.

"Mr. Henry Rowe Schoolcraft, General Lewis Cass," said the Major.

Governor Cass's hand clasped Henry's in a hearty grip. "We meet under more amiable circumstances, Schoolcraft," he said. "You see me free of the ague and deep in our problems. Come—sit down."

Major Forsyth drew forward a chair.

Soon Henry found himself sitting beside the Governor, facing the map which Cass had been studying.

"Now, then," continued the Governor, "we're to set out as soon as possible for the northern boundary along the lake. We have several purposes in mind. I'll come to them in a moment. See here—" Now he indicated Detroit on the crude, hand-drawn map before him—"this is where we are, and here we go along—" His finger traced the way up through Lake St. Clair, along the River St. Clair, up the coast of Lake Huron to the great island of Michilimackinac.

From there the Governor's stubby finger pushed on among the islands, up the River of St. Mary, through the Sault de Ste. Marie into the bay of Lake Superior, and then on along the shore of that lake to the foot of Superior, from which the way led into an unmarked region where the Mississippi was said to begin its flow toward the Gulf of Mexico. It was at this place in the map that the Governor's finger made a small circle.

"Here is where we reach our goal, Schoolcraft," he said.

"And what is that, Mr. Cass?"

"We have more than one—but for you, this is the one. Zebulon Pike believed that the Mississippi River takes its rise in Leech Lake. There are Indians who tell us that there is a blue water beyond that lake, and it is there that the Mississippi has its source. A 'hidden water,' they call it. Sometimes 'a piece of sky' lost among the hills and forests. Mr. Schoolcraft, I hope that you will be able to find that hidden piece of sky for us."

"I shall try, Mr. Cass," said Henry. But he was filled with doubt. For one thing, the map showed nothing at all that looked helpful. "The map is very vague," he went on.

"True. But I have another, though I cannot vouch for its correctness."

As he spoke, the Governor moved away the larger map. There beneath it on the table lay a small piece of birch-bark, on which lines were crudely drawn in red. Henry thought at first that this map was drawn in blood, but then he saw that it was done in the juice of some berry. So the Indians had drawn it. He bent to look closely at it.

It was the map of one large stream and many small ones. There were also many lakes. The large stream flowed through many of the lakes. It flowed out of the southwest, into the north, then to the east, then to the south, and was lost going in that direction at the end of the piece of bark. The drawing was so crude that Henry could not be sure just where the great river began. But it looked to be at a lake someone had named "La Biche." The writing of that word was clearly not in the hand of the artist who had drawn the map.

Governor Cass explained. "It would seem from this map that the origin of the Mississippi is in Lake La Biche. But I must tell you that 'La Biche' is a voyageur's name, given to many bodies of water. Freely translated, it means hind or roe—'Deer Lake' would do as well as any other name. While it's plainly enough marked on this map, two voyageurs who have looked at it tell me there are no less than four lakes of the same name in that region. The map is thus, I fear, not of much help. But it does tell us that Pike was wrong."

"May I make a copy of this map, sir?"

"I would expect you to."

"I don't want to fail this mission. Only in July of last year I stood at the mouth of the Father of Waters. Now I should like to reach its source. I doubt if there is any other man who will have been at both ends of the Mississippi within a year's time."

"Well said, Mr. Schoolcraft! Further, the country will be new to you, and you will have opportunity to study its geology."

"I have already read everything I could lay my hands on that dealt with the Northwest Territory, Governor."

"Good!" exclaimed the Governor. "You see, sir, this

project is dear to my heart. But I have had to promise Mr. Calhoun many other things—a geological report, for instance. That is in your hands, also. Captain Douglass and Mr. Chase will be expected not only to map the expedition, but also to report on the zoology and botany of the Territory."

"You mentioned more than one goal, sir," said Henry.

"So I did. There are wider causes that command our attention. For one, we shall want to find out more about the Indian tribes along the way. Specifically, we shall want to know to what extent they are still trading with the British, who, I am afraid, have a habit of conniving against us. The late war with the British is but a few years done, and our route is uncomfortably close to Canada. You have heard of Lord Selkirk?"

"He has a colony of some kind at Pembina above the Red River of the North."

"You have indeed made yourself familiar with information, Mr. Schoolcraft!" said the Governor in a pleased voice. "He has set himself up more strongly than ever, and he has the allegiance of many Indians. Yet, as you know, our government passed a law in 1816 forbidding trade between our nationals and those of another country."

"It has been of great help to the American Fur Company," said Schoolcraft.

Governor Cass smiled. "I have no doubt Mr. Astor had a hand in its passage," he went on. "But there are other matters that require our attention. We are especially anxious to obtain a piece of Indian land at the Straits of St. Mary's to establish a garrison there. Finally, we shall want a look at the Copper Rock—sometimes called the copper mines—up the Ontonagon River from Lake Superior. That, too, is your field. I understand you've already ordered hammers from our armorer."

Henry smiled. "They keep you well informed, Governor."

Governor Cass laughed contentedly. "I have to know about the littlest things as well as the biggest, if I am to govern well so large a Territory as this of Michigan." He grew serious again. "How many members of the expedition have you met?"

"None, sir, apart from my companions from Buffalo. Except, of course, yourself."

"And Major Forsyth here. Ah, well, there will doubtless be time for you to meet them before we get started. Unhappily, there are often delays we have not counted on."

"I hope we will begin the journey soon, sir. I am eager to be gone."

"No more than I, Schoolcraft. The trouble is, we're still waiting for our canoes. I ordered them from the

Indians quite a while ago. Oh, they'll be along, but only when the Indians think they're fit for use. I trust you yourself are ready?"

"Except for my hammers."

Major Forsyth, who had gone out of the room, came in and said, "Captain Douglass and Mr. Chase are here, sir."

Governor Cass stood up and shook hands once more with Henry. "We shall see each other soon again. I hope you've not forgotten that we're to dine together here today."

"No, sir, I haven't."

Governor Cass turned and made a sign to Major Forsyth, who came forward to see Henry to the door at the same time as he went to usher in Henry's companions of the journey.

*   *   *

It was longer than Henry had thought before the expedition was ready.

One week passed, then another. The month of May was almost gone when, finally, one day, the word went around that the Chippewas of Lake Huron had brought in the canoes ordered for the party. No sooner were the canoes at hand than all the members of the expedition were notified that the launching was to take place the next day.

On the morning of the twenty-fourth, they gathered at the water's edge. There they all were, except for Governor Cass, who had gone on ahead with a party of friends, led by General Macomb, who commanded the militia of the Territory. They had driven overland to Grosse Pointe, where the Governor would join the expedition.

Long before the day of departure, during the waiting weeks, Henry had met all his traveling companions. The most energetic of them was James Doty, scarcely twenty. He had moved to Detroit from Martinsburg, New York, two years ago, and was already practising law in that city, and was the clerk of the Supreme Court of the Territory. He was an eager, open-faced young fellow, filled with enthusiasm for the journey. He had large, liquid blue eyes, a high, dome-like forehead, and a full-lipped mouth. He told Henry at once that he, too, would keep a record of the trip.

Charlie Trowbridge, who was to be Captain Douglass's assistant, was Doty's roommate. He was just out of his teens, He was a dark, enthusiastic lad. He seemed to look upon Doty as a rival, and always tried to outdo Doty in everything he did. He wore a frank, innocent look, and candidly looked on the expedition as a lark. Doty, on the other hand, seemed a farsighted young man, for he spoke all the time of the northwestern frontier, and speculated on how long it would take to develop it.

These matters did not seem to interest Charlie Trowbridge at all.

The party had to have a doctor, in case there was trouble with the Indians or someone took sick, or they had
an accident with the canoes. They were going into unknown country; there was no telling what they might
find and what manner of dangers they might meet. So
Governor Cass had picked young Dr. Alexander Wolcott, an army surgeon, a short man, with a tendency to
stoutness. He was young, like the others. He kept very
much to himself, and preserved a dignified mien, as if he
thought this befitted the expedition's doctor.

Finally, there was Lt. Aeneas Mackay. He was in command of the seven soldiers who were making the trip. He
was tall and stocky. Though he liked to smile, there was
an air of firmness about him. It was plain to see, Henry
thought, that Lt. Mackay would not stand for any nonsense.

In addition to these members of the expedition,
Governor Cass had personally chosen ten Canadian voyageurs and ten Indians, Ottawa and Shawnee, with two
men—Joseph Parks and James Riley—to serve as guides
and interpreters. The whole party, by Henry's count,
amounted to thirty-eight people. But it was hard to make
a certain count, for the shore was crowded. It seemed as
if the whole population of Detroit had come down to

watch the preparations for the voyage. Henry had never seen anything so colorful.

The voyageurs wore gaily colored sashes and caps. The Indians were resplendent; they had put on all their brightest ornaments of beads, cloth, and feathers. Even before the other members of the expedition gathered at the shore, the voyageurs and the Indians had begun to load the canoes.

And what splendid craft the canoes were! Henry had never seen their like. They were so big that each could carry eight paddlers, in addition to two tons or more of provisions. They were made of white birch bark. The bark had been peeled in large sheets and bent over a slender frame of cedar ribs. It was held together by gunwales, and kept apart by slender bars of cedar. The bark was sewn around these with the thin, fine roots of young spruce trees. The Indians called these fine roots *wattap*. This same flexible thread that the Indians used on their baskets, made the gunwales of the canoes look like the rims of Indian baskets.

The canoes were made watertight by pitch pine, thickened by boiling until it was a kind of gum. In the third bar across from the bow, a place was cut for a mast, so that a sail could be hoisted whenever the wind was favorable. Then the paddlers would have a chance to rest. There were seats for the paddlers. These were strips of board, suspended by cords from the gunwales. All the paddles were the light kind used by the Indians. They were made of cedar, as was the large, long-handled and broad-bladed paddle used by the steersman.

Each of the canoes carried not only a sail, but a small standard on which were the arms of the United States. This standard indicated that this was a government expedition. In addition, each canoe had a kind of tent on it, made with an oilcloth, to keep the provisions dry in case of rain.

Seeing Henry gazing at the flags, Doty paused beside him and said, "Do you know, Schoolcraft, this will be the first time the United States flag is flown officially over some of the territory we plan to cross."

"Then that's why the Governor insists they be kept flying."

"Right. The Indians must learn to recognize our flag. They've known the British flag too long."

It was plain to be seen that the canoes were not going to be ready for hours. Though the men had started loading at once, it would be afternoon before the expedition could get under way, for the shore was still lined with the supplies they were to take.

There were things Henry had not dreamed they would need. There were over a hundred pounds of powder, more of lead, and almost a quarter-of-a-hundred pounds of shot. There were yards of chintz, calico, silk, ribbons, coarse blankets, and the like, in addition to shoes, shawls, hats, cotton stuff, thread, coat buttons— all gifts to show their friendship for the Indians they would meet. These gifts took up much space in the canoes.

Most important of all were the materials for repairs, and the food they would need until they could restock supplies at the posts along the way. Legging binding, a medicine chest, flints, sugar, beef—over seven hundred pounds of bacon alone! Spoons, knives and forks, pepper boxes, gun locks, dried beef, corn meal, butter, bundles of bark in case anything went wrong with the canoes as well as a hundred-and-forty pounds of gum, thirty bundles of wattap, forty paddles, three masts, twelve poles— all for the same purpose. Henry stopped trying to estimate all their supplies, though he wanted to set it all down in his journal, so that if ever he went alone into the wilderness, he would know his needs.

Like the other members of the expedition, Henry helped load the canoes, too. He was not very good at it. Compared to the skilled Indians and voyageurs, he was awkward, indeed. This was partly due to his lack of experience, and partly because he could not help watching the Indians. What strange people Indians were! Every day since he had landed at Detroit he found his interest in them growing stronger.

The soldiers were not helping at the canoes. They

were loading a large schooner which stood off shore. This schooner was intended to carry the greater part of the supplies to Michilimackinac, to wait the party's arrival at that post.

It was four o'clock in the afternoon before the loading was completed, and the men were ordered to take their places in the canoes.

Looking around him, Henry was certain that everyone in Detroit had come down to see them off. People filled the distance from the river's edge to the houses and the streets well away from the water. When it was plain that the expedition was getting started at last, the people set up a great shouting and cheering, waving their handkerchiefs and hats to bid them good-by.

There was excitement right at the start, for the Indians, who had their own canoe, dared the voyageurs to race along the river. The Indians darted ahead at once and held the lead until the long pull began to tell on them; then the voyageurs caught up and passed them.

Joseph Parks, the interpreter, a lantern-jawed fellow sat in the same canoe with Henry. Seeing how interested Henry was, he leaned forward with a broad grin and spoke.

"D'you see, Mr. Schoolcraft—that's the Indians all over. They gits dragged out easy. Big and bold as the wind at start, but in no time at all they're done in."

"What are they shouting?" asked Henry, for the Indians were shouting at the voyageurs, as they had done all along the course of the race.

"They make fun of the white men." Parks shrugged. "Indians like to make big talk. But it takes them Canucks on the long haul."

"Where did you learn their language, Parks?"

"Me? Didn't have no leeway, I guess. I was forced to it, as you might say, when the Shawnees took me prisoner years ago. Got so's I could talk Shawnee an' Ottawa an' Chippewa. You listen to Kewa-schosum. You hear what he says?"

Chief Kewa-schosum was the Ottawa who was in command of the Indians in their canoe. Every little while his voice rang out in a guttural command. His words sounded more like grunts.

Parks chuckled. "He says 'Slow' and 'Fast' and 'To right.' That's what he says."

Henry realized that Parks would be an invaluable companion on the long journey, since he and the other guide, Riley, were the only white men who could speak the Indian languages at all well.

They had pulled well away from the crowds by this time. Now Henry turned and looked to the shore. It surprised him anew to see how settled this country looked. There were not even woods in sight along the river, except for the many wooded islands in it, all now green with leaves and grass. All the shore was well cultivated.

Except for one or two trees now and then along the water's edge, the only trees were orchards. Windmills rose at every prominent point along the river, and all the way there were farms.

He looked back toward the point where Detroit receded into the skyline. How long would it be, he wondered, before they would again see a civilized settlement? There were forts along the way, Henry knew—but towns? In all his reading in the works of Carver and other travelers, he could not remember reading of towns beyond Detroit.

He did not know what lay ahead, though he reasoned that there must be some kind of settlement around the fort on Michilimackinac. But here, all was mild and beautiful. Before them, Henry felt sure, all was equally beautiful, but it was wild and unknown.

Not once did they slacken speed and soon they passed out into Lake St. Clair.

In two hours they had reached Grosse Pointe. It had not taken them as long as Henry had expected.

Governor Cass and his friends were waiting for them. The Governor led his suite in a great cheer as the canoes came in toward the land. Then he himself helped them to disembark and carry their provisions up on the point to the place chosen for the camp. Then he bade his friends good-by and took his place as a member of the expedition.

At last, Henry thought, they were all together. The nine-mile trip from Detroit to Grosse Pointe had been more like a trial run. Now the trip would begin in earnest, and soon they would be far from the environs of Detroit, deep in the heart of that unknown country of lakes and rivers, of wilderness and Indians, which was their destination.

Fort Gratiot

WHEN THEY LEFT Grosse Pointe at noon of the second day, Henry rode in the Governor's canoe. So did Parks. Henry had hoped that he might be near Parks, so that he could call on him to tell him about the Indians. Henry was disappointed, however, that Alex Chase was not in his canoe, but Alex had been assigned to help Captain Douglass make maps of the expedition's route, so he had to ride in the same canoe as Douglass.

After a day and a half spent on Grosse Pointe, all were delighted that the long journey had been resumed.

They had been late in getting started for the severe cold and a strong head wind had kept them from launching the canoes. But "There'll be other delays," warned the Governor. "One can count on nothing. We can hope only that we're not delayed too long at any one place. It freezes early in these regions to which we're going."

"But it's only May," protested Henry. "The frost has only now left the ground!"

"By the time we find ourselves back in Detroit, many of the places we have visited will have known frost and ice."

"And what if we should get caught?"

Governor Cass shrugged his shoulders in a way that meant no one could tell what might happen then, but the chances that they would get back alive were not good.

"The land trails are very hard, Schoolcraft," he explained. "We might have to depend on the kindness of the Chippewas. They might see us through. They might not. Even then, if we weren't near a village, we could perish before we reached one. The wilderness is a supreme challenge to men, my young friend."

Nevertheless, Henry was not alarmed. Frost and cold seemed far away; ice and snow had been left behind by the season, even though the mercury had read a chilly fifty degrees on that first night at Grosse Pointe.

The journey on which he was embarking was very different from the one he had made when he came to

Detroit from New York. That way had been through settled country, where every woodland area opened on farm land or villages. The way ahead lay through hundreds upon hundreds of miles of unbroken wilderness, where the only openings were small breaks in the wilderness for forts, or for the encampments and settlements of the Indians. The difference did not frighten him; he traveled with a light heart.

Yet, before the day was done, he had reason to remember the Governor's warning. Just when they were in the middle of Lake St. Clair, making for the mouth of the St. Clair River, up which they hoped to go to Lawson's Island for the night, a sudden wind sprang up. Soon the waves were breaking across the canoe. The men who were not paddling had to take turns bailing out the water. So great was the strength of the wind, that instead of making four miles an hour, a heavily loaded canoe was lucky to make half that distance.

When they finally reached Lawson's island at ten o'clock at night, the men were exhausted. They were wet and cold. Moreover, once again the temperature had fallen. Henry began to understand what the Governor meant by his warning of weather danger. If wind and rain made them so miserable, what might not bitter cold and snow do to them!

Early next morning the tired men were on their way again.

At this point the St. Clair River was a stream almost three-quarters of a mile wide. Slowly the canoes worked their way upstream. Now and then they passed larger vessels at anchor, though there seemed to be no settlements in sight.

"Why are they here?" asked Henry at last.

"They are ships of provisions and sometimes troops for the forts at Michilimackinac, Green Bay, and Chicago," explained the Governor. "This wind is a little too strong for them."

Henry discovered that it was the custom of the frontier country to hail or salute every craft they passed. It did not matter whether it was a ship or small canoe. Thus, at every ship, the Governor stood up, identified himself, and asked whether he could be of any help. And every time canoes of Indians came down river, Parks or Riley talked with them.

The more he saw of the Indians, the more curious Henry grew about the way they lived. He knew very little about them, only what Carver had written of them in some detail, and what he had read of them in other sources. He had come to think of them as little more than children. Sometimes he thought them very ignorant; then they would give evidence of great wisdom. It was most confusing. So he began to pay more and more attention to the Indians they saw.

Most of the canoes that went by contained just one

family of Indians. They were either Ottawa or Chippewa Indians. Both these tribes were friendly to white men. Each canoe usually carried the Indians' blankets, guns, fishing apparatus—and dogs!

The Indians were not only willing but eager to stop and talk. Parks explained this by saying scornfully, "They might get presents." Though Parks seemed to be scornful of the Indians he grudgingly showed admiration for them. Henry could not understand this conflicting attitude.

Once in a while one of the Indians recognized the Governor. They called him by their own name for him, "Big Belly." This was not a term of disrespect, but only one they felt was a fair description of the Governor. It did not offend Governor Cass. If anything, it seemed to please him when they recognized him. To the Governor, the Indians were clearly just as much his charge as the white men. He considered them adults and thus obliged to obey the laws of the Territory just as the white men did.

With Parks' help, Henry soon learned to pick out the different kinds of tribal decoration, and the different ways in which various tribesmen dressed. It was not long before he could tell a Chippewa from an Ottawa or a Shawnee. When traveling, Chippewas wore less clothing than the others. Usually, only the chiefs dressed up. Their ornaments and decorations marked their rank.

Some of the chiefs proudly wore broadcloth coats which had been given them by white men.

The Indians seemed to respect their leaders very much, and always obeyed any order given by the chieftain. Indeed, Henry could not help thinking that Indian leaders won more respect from their followers than white leaders did.

Henry looked in vain for furs in the canoes they passed. Where were the Indians going, if not to bring furs to market, he asked Parks.

"The Indians, they like to move 'round," explained Parks. "If the tribe don't go, they pack up, go by themselves."

"You mean they've got all their belongings with them?" Henry asked.

The Governor, who had overheard their conversation, interrupted. "Probably all they own, yes. Sometimes, if the tribe is in a village they know will stay where it is for some time, they'll leave their wigwam or lodge to stand for their return."

"They do go back, then?"

"Most of the time, yes. Those who have families find it better to live with the village. They get back in time for the hunting season. The lone wolves—the braves who have no wives or children—they sometimes go it alone. But many of the lone wolves are renegades who've been driven from the villages for disobeying a law. They may be dangerous, because they've been cast out by their tribes."

"Why are they cast out?" asked Henry, wonderingly.

"There's not much room in the wilderness for hardy individualists. Indians must obey their chiefs for the good of the whole tribe. If they disobey, they might bring trouble upon the whole tribe. The chiefs feel that they are responsible if a member of their tribe causes trouble—so long as that member is still in the tribe. So, if one shows rebellion—if he breaks the Indian laws—he is cast out from the tribe, and the chief's responsibility ends."

This was a different way of life from any Henry had known. Yet, it was very simple. It was one which had very much to be said in praise of it. He looked over every canoe load of Indians they met with keen interest. What strange human beings they were! But certainly human beings! They were always anxious to stop and talk, and perhaps barter a little, but their women were silent. They sat and never said a word. Their dogs barked at everything. Sometimes a canoe had almost as many dogs in it as Indians.

"You're interested in the Indians, Henry?" asked the Governor presently.

"Yes, sir. I hadn't thought I would be. I suppose it's just that they're so strange to me. I find it difficult to imagine how they live—and yet they seem to have social laws just as we do, but laws and ways fitted to the wilderness."

"They do. Sometimes they endure near starvation and much misery. But each of them knows more about the air and the earth and the water and all the things on the earth than any one of us—even you, Henry, with your special kind of knowledge."

"Would they not be interesting to study?" Henry wondered.

"Study them, by all means. To you, they're strange. I've accepted them long ago. They have a right to their way of life, just as we have to ours. Who shall say which is the better? Remember, they've lived in their fashion for a long time before white men came to bother them. The Indians must have been here for centuries before Columbus set foot on these shores. And they've survived."

The St. Clair River seemed to Henry as full of traffic as the streams of the East had been. This was not yet, then, the wilderness he had imagined. But so many of his ideas about this country were being changed, perhaps his concept of the wilderness would change, too.

When they came upon the ship which was carrying their supplies to Michilimackinac, the Governor recognized it at once and gave a sharp order to swing in toward shore. He wanted to talk with the captain.

Henry got out and walked along the stony shore. At

once he became the geologist. He picked up stones here and there to examine them. In a kind of little bay, he found some carnelian, which he put into his pocket. Several times he took out his hammers and split the stones, so that he could study them better.

The Ottawas and the Shawnees who were curious about what he did, followed on his heels. Every time they saw him pick up a particular kind of stone, they hurried and hunted for others like it. As soon as they had found such stones, they came to press them upon Henry, wondering what he would do.

The little hammers fascinated them. They had never seen anything like them. They had never before seen a man who broke apart stones like this. Soon, whenever they spoke to him, they called him by a strange name— "Paw-gwa-be-can-e-ga." It sounded impressive, and they spoke his new name with respect.

"What are they calling me?" Henry asked Parks.

"Destroyer of Rocks," answered Parks. "Rock-Breaker. Indians are very sharp when they name people. They come right to the point."

Henry grinned. He wished there were some way he could express his pleasure to the Indians for giving him a name of his own among them. If only he could speak their language!

But now the Governor was hallooing for them, and they hurried back to the canoes.

Late in the day, they came to their first rapids. Henry had been noticing how clear the water was. He had been watching the ducks, the plovers, and the snipes which moved about, on and over the water. Then suddenly he had seen foam and lines of bubbles, and, looking ahead, he saw the white froth of the rapids.

Soon he learned how skillful the voyageurs were. The rapids looked very dangerous, but the voyageurs never hesitated. They pushed the canoes ahead without once faltering, and in a moment they were in the midst of the churning water, feeling the spray of it on their hands and faces. They were tossed this way and that as the steersmen guided the canoes through the rough water.

Henry glanced at the Governor. He sat immovable. There was not a trace of concern on his face. Yet Henry thought that at any moment they might strike a rock and overturn. But Governor Cass was not worried. The only time any expression at all crossed his face was at the approach of one of the other canoes. The canoe came near enough to be touched, and, if it did touch, an accident might result. The Governor watched it with sharp, wary eyes. But all was well.

For some time they had been passing between walls of trees. Though there had been occasional houses in which French traders and farmers lived down toward the mouth of the river, these had long since given place to forests. Now Henry saw, at the head of the rapids they were traversing, a higher bank on which stood a building that was clearly a fort, for the American flag flew over the stockade.

This was Fort Gratiot, the place of their encampment for the night.

Beyond the fort lay Lake Huron.

The voyageurs mastered the rapids and swung the canoes in toward the shore. The maneuver required all their efforts, for the river was very swift at this place, and the current washed hard against the south bank.

Their arrival had been watched from the fort. A detachment of men led by Major Cummings, the fort's commander, was already riding out from the stockade to greet them.

Seeing them, the Governor smiled. "We're lucky to have Mr. Calhoun as the stepfather of our expedition," he said. "He's sent word to all the military posts to do everything they can to aid us."

His words were almost drowned out in the roar of the guns as the detachment of soldiers fired a salute. The Ottawas and Shawnees cried out in alarm.

As the canoes touched land Major Cummings stepped smartly forward. He saluted. "We are at your service, Governor."

Governor Cass returned the Major's salute and stepped to the shore.

Everything was now astir with the bustle to which Henry was growing accustomed. The men leaped out of the canoes, eager to follow the welcoming company of soldiers and their leader. The Major, accompanied by the Governor, was already walking toward the stockade. The voyageurs and the Indians busied themselves, securing the canoes for the night, while the other members of the expedition followed the Governor.

Henry saw at once that Fort Gratiot was not large. There were signs to show that it was a recently constructed post. It enclosed a magazine, barracks, and other lesser buildings. Though it had been built to accommodate a garrison of one batallion, it was occupied by a company of sixty men. On one side of the stockade, forty acres of land had been broken for beans and grain. These were meant to be added to the army rations.

Inside, except where the buildings stood, there were the remains of an older fort. It was an ideal place for a fort, for, from the wall of the stockade, up which Henry went before it grew too dark to see, the approach to Lake Huron was in sight. The fort commanded the entrance into the river, too.

"The *Coureurs du Bois* put up the first fort here," explained the Governor at their evening meal. "That was

when the French owned all the land. Then the French
Government took it over and called it Fort St. Joseph.
But they abandoned it and had it burned in the summer
of 1688."

"Then this fort is new," said Henry.

"Fort Gratiot was built only six years ago."

After supper, Major Cummings and Lieutenant Hunt
of the fort came to pay their respects anew to the party.
But few of the travelers were lively enough to talk very
much. Those who rode in the canoes were almost as tired
as the paddlers. In some cases, they were more tired, as
was Henry. The voyageurs were used to such hard work,
and to the cramped positions in the canoes, while the
others were not. Most of them were too tired to make
any effort to be good hosts, so the officers soon returned
to the fort so that the encampment could sleep.

At eight in the morning, they were off once more.

There was still half-a-mile of fast water to travel. The
river, here, flowed at the rate of seven miles an hour,
against which the canoes made slow headway. But at last
they rode out on to Lake Huron.

Before them lay water that stretched as far as the eye
could see. On their left was the flat shore of the Territory of Michigan, a shore that was covered with trees.
White pines, poplars, and birch trees crowded down to
the water's edge. This was the coast of the lake they were
to follow for several days.

Henry gazed in awe. He had never before seen so large a body of inland water. Indeed, had he been a wilderness explorer, he might have thought he had reached the ocean.

Swiftly they shot forward over the placid water of the lake.

Now, at last, they were leaving behind them the last frontier of settlement and plunging into the vast, silent wilderness. None knew what they might find.

The White Rock

ON THE SIXTH DAY of their journey, and the second after they had entered Lake Huron, for the first time they passed a break in the monotony of the flat shore line. This was a great white rock, which showed up clearly against the sky at the end of a long, clay bank. They were at this point about sixty miles above Fort Gratiot.

Henry saw the rock, but he would not have spoken of it had not Parks motioned to draw his attention to it.

"Watch them," said Parks.

Henry was puzzled for a moment by his meaning. But

then he understood that Parks meant for him to watch the Indians, passing in their canoes. He saw that these Indians made a kind of detour to touch on the shore nearest the white rock. Some of them left their canoes and went into the woods toward the rock.

The Governor looked inquiringly at Henry and grinned.

"What is it?" asked Henry.

He sensed that there was something about the rock they thought he might like to know.

"They make sacrifice at the rock," explained Parks.

"Why?"

Parks shrugged. "Me, I don't know. They b'lieve many things. To them, the white rock is different. Maybe it's not natural. So they think Manitou has put it there."

"Manitou is their god?" asked Henry.

"Manitou is the Great Spirit," answered Parks.

Governor Cass interrupted. "They have many manitous, Schoolcraft. There are good and bad manitous. They are at caves, at waterfalls, at rocks—wherever the Indians' eyes are drawn to see something different or strange. In this they are like children. Whatever they don't understand, they fear. Like some of us. They don't take chances; they make offerings at all such places."

"What kind of offerings?"

The Governor shrugged. "Carrot tobacco, mostly."

Parks added, "Sometimes a beaver skin, or a knife or hatchet—even arm bands of silver."

To Henry this was more than a matter of amusement or idle curiosity. This was another face of the Indians' different way of life. Henry knew that once upon a time many hundreds of years ago, white men had done similar things. They too had left offerings before trees, at caves, at great mounds of rock. This was a custom of primitive, undeveloped peoples. He pressed for more knowledge. He wanted to know much more than either the Governor or the interpreter could tell him.

"Do they make special journeys to make offerings at such places?" he asked.

Parks shook his head. "No. Only when they pass by. An' not always then. It is jus' when they feel they mus' do so."

"They have enough manitous so that they need never go out of their way," said the Governor. "Keep your eyes open when we go ashore. You never know when we might find offerings—at trees, beside lakes and pools."

"They are never disturbed?"

"No Indian would disturb an offering to Manitou. He would be afraid for his life."

"He would think Manitou would find him an' punish him," added Parks.

So the Indians, too, feared to do wrong! The Indians

seemed daily less and less savage. The picture he had had in his mind of howling, dancing, painted creatures, half man, half savage, was fading fast. Already he was beginning to feel a little silly because he had so easily accepted travelers' tales. More and more, the Indians were beginning to strike Henry as fellow human beings, and he remembered that not all travelers wrote lurid stories about them. Some of the travelers referred to the Indians as "red brothers."

As the white rock receded into the distance, Henry began to look forward more keenly than ever to the first Indian village they might see. Then he could discover for himself some of the strange customs of this wilderness dweller, who excited so much fear and wonder in the cities of the East.

*   *   *

Four days later, Henry had his first sight of an Indian village.

The expedition, after having been held back several days by violent winds and thunder showers, reached the Au Sable River across Saginaw Bay. They were not quite half way to Michilimackinac. On the shore of the river, where the canoes put in, was a band of Chippewa Indians. At their head was an Indian chief. At first these Indians did not appear to see the party. They faded into the woods and were gone by the time the party reached the shore.

"They watch us," said Parks.

"They looked like a hunting party," said Doty, with the wisdom of one who had lived long enough in the Territory to know.

"Possibly," agreed the Governor. "In any case, they're not far from their village, and as soon as they recognize me, they'll come in, never fear."

In this, Governor Cass was right.

Scarcely had the tents been pitched for the party, when the Indians appeared once more. The chief, who introduced himself to the Governor as Black Eagle, had evidently gone back to his village and dressed more formally. He had changed from his hunting costume into new clothes which clearly marked his rank. His headdress had been increased to one of many feathers. He wore a beaded band across one shoulder and a military band across the other. He had painted himself up more brilliantly.

He and his braves were very friendly. Henry wondered how they would meet the Ottawas and Shawnees with the expedition. Would they be happy to see other Indians, or not?

Much to Henry's surprise, they were even more casual than parties of white men, meeting in similar circumstances, would have been. They could not speak with any ease together, because of differences of language. It was just as if neither of them existed for the other.

But for the Governor and his party, the Chippewas had an entirely different approach. First Black Eagle made a speech to the Governor. He spoke in his own language. Parks, who sat cross-legged near Henry, translated. Black Eagle said he was glad to see this great friend of the red men. They had heard that the Governor was coming. The Chippewas had ways of sending such knowledge on ahead. Now they hoped that the Governor would visit their village so that he could see and relieve their wants.

"They're always in want, just as much when their lodges are full as when they are empty," said Doty at Henry's side.

Parks grinned and nodded in agreement.

"They always want something for nothing," Doty went on. "But, of course, there are white men like that, too."

His speech concluded, Black Eagle did not wait for a reply from Governor Cass. He immediately produced a pipe of peace, took a puff from it, and then handed it to the Governor, who in turn handed it around to everyone present. Even Henry and Doty had to take a puff from the pipe. The strong, acrid smoke made them cough, which delighted the Indians.

When everyone had taken a puff from the pipe, Black Eagle began to shake hands all around. Henry was astonished to see this handshaking.

"Have they learned this from white men?" he asked.

Doty shrugged. "No one knows. They've been doing it as long as I've been in the Territory."

"They do this a long time," added Parks.

The ceremonies finished, the Indians waited on the Governor's reply.

Governor Cass thanked them for their welcome to him and his party. Then he said he was sorry, he would not have time to visit the village of the Chippewas, even if it was only two miles up the river. But he had gifts for his red children.

He signaled to some of the soldiers, who came forward with tobacco they carried along for just such occasions as this. Black Eagle accepted it with many words and gestures of gratitude. Then he in turn made signs to certain young men of his party. They brought forward some fresh sturgeons they had caught and presented them to the Governor.

After this, Governor Cass went on with his speech. He said that though he himself could not go to visit their village, he would send three members of his party with Black Eagle. He named Parks, Doty and Schoolcraft, with a sidelong glance at Henry. The Governor's eyes were twinkling as he indicated to the chief which three members of his party were to go with the Chippewas.

The chief immediately presented himself to the three of them. He looked a little puzzled. He did not know whether they understood his language, but he appeared to recognize Parks. He tried him with a few words. Parks answered in the Chippewa tongue. Then Black Eagle was satisfied and began to talk rapidly.

The chief explained that they should go at once, before it was dark. It was not far, but the white men tired easily. Besides, he said, darkness would make it harder to travel on foot.

Though Henry was already very tired, he was pleased at the thought of seeing the Chippewa village. Doty and Parks were less enthusiastic, though Doty was more amiable than Parks, who grumbled with discontent. Parks had gone with the Governor many times to visit Indian villages, and for too long a time in his youth he had been a prisoner in one of them. But he and Doty got to their feet with Henry.

All three followed the Chippewas out of the circle around Governor Cass, who sat grinning after them, as if he had played a trick on them. They moved out toward the woods.

Henry had expected to find horses outside the glow of the campfire, but there were none. They were meant to walk to the village. Parks explained that few of the Chippewas owned horses, especially in this part of the Territory. Farther west, where the Indians of the Plains flourished, horses were plentiful. They needed them there, in order to travel. But these Chippewas were mostly river dwellers and traveled by canoe.

Black Eagle took the lead.

The way wound through the woods up along the Au Sable River. Though the forest was dense, the path was well defined. It had been used repeatedly by the Indians going to and from Lake Huron and along the shore, to hunt. The Indians lost no time. They did not actually walk, but proceeded at a quick gait which was halfway between a run and a walk. At this rate of speed, the distance to the village did not seem as long as it was. But Henry and Doty were winded by the pace.

In less than half an hour, they were in the Chippewa village.

It was not a large settlement. It consisted of only a dozen lodges—long, low buildings, made of stone and bark. They were usually in the shape of a rectangle, but one or two resembled wigwams. They were neatly arranged around an open place where a large fire burned. At the arrival of the party, all the women vanished into the lodges. Only the warriors remained outside, together with so many dogs that Henry thought there must be more dogs than Indians.

As he led them around the village, Black Eagle talked rapidly, with many motions of hands and arms. Parks translated most of what he said for Henry and Doty. Doty understood a little of it himself, but not much.

The chief complained of the same things of which he had spoken to Governor Cass. The Chippewas, he insisted, were short of provisions. They needed help from the White Father, by whom they meant the Governor, who was the representative of the Great White Father, the President.

"They'd just as soon get provisions without working for them if the Governor were fool enough to hand them out. But he isn't," said Doty.

Henry remarked that Doty did not seem to like the Indians.

Doty shook his head vigorously in denial. "No, that isn't it. I wouldn't try to judge them. They live differently. Only I know that I'll have to deal with them. My future is here in this country, and I know how many of them there are."

Black Eagle, who did not understand English, waited respectfully until Doty and Henry finished talking. Then he went on.

They walked through the village from one end to the other. Black Eagle thought he was impressing them with their needs. He acted confident and sure of himself. Doty wore an air of amiable tolerance. Parks went through it all as if a punishment had been inflicted on him. Henry kept his eyes and ears open.

He could see that the village was not very permanent. He asked about this.

Doty said, "I don't think it's meant to be permanent."

Parks agreed. "They build it to live in two, three year. Maybe five. Then the lodges they need fixing. By this time, all the hunting an' fishing been done. So why fix the lodges? They jus' move on to new place."

"That practice seems to be common to all the Indians I've known, not only with the Chippewas," added Doty.

Wherever they walked, Henry noticed that the ornaments and utensils—everything the Chippewas used—were fashioned with great skill. They were not just put together, but made with an eye for their attractiveness. There were few signs of the white man in this village. Once Henry saw the muzzle of a gun sticking out from beneath a blanket on the floor of a lodge, but there was little else to connect these Indians with the traders.

Indian children peered out of the lodges as they went by. Sometimes Black Eagle swept away a door-covering of animal skin, and allowed the two guests to look into the lodge where the squaws, the old people, and the children sat along the walls. The floors, Henry noticed, were of earth. Very little food was to be seen. The chief evidently had the privilege of entering any lodge; his word was the village's absolute law.

Now it was dusk, and their visit was over.

On the way back to their own camp, Henry spoke of

the absence of provisions. "I have to admit, I didn't see much food," he said.

Parks and Doty laughed. Doty said, "They've hidden their supplies. That's why the Governor wouldn't come. He's wise to all their tricks, and they know, but they try it just the same. It's second nature to them."

"When the sentinels report who comes, Black Eagle give order to hide the provisions so he can try to fool the Governor into giving him more," said Parks.

Black Eagle, who had caught the sound of his name as the white men spoke it, grinned and nodded with pleasure. He did not understand what had been said.

Back at the expedition's camp, Henry would have begun a report to Governor Cass immediately. But the Governor stopped him with an upraised hand.

"Spare me, Henry," he said. "I only hope you've learned a little about the way our red brethren live. I already know how it is with them, and our own Indians could probably lead the way to the caches in the woods where Black Eagle's Chippewas have hidden their provisions. That, too, is part of their way of life."

So Henry knew that Governor Cass had sent him along only so that he might see the Chippewa village and learn a little more about the Indians, in whom he had shown such an interest. His visit had only served to whet his appetite for more. He could have forgotten that he had come on the expedition as a geologist.

Michilimackinac

ON THE AFTERNOON of the fourteenth day of their journey, they entered the harbor of Michilimackinac.

Henry would never forget his first sight of the great turtle, as the voyageurs called Michilimackinac. As the canoe rounded the southwestern shore of Bois Blanc Island, preparing to skirt the entrance into Lake Michigan and drive across the lake still farther into the northwest, Henry saw high bluffs struck sharply against the sky ahead. They were rugged against the heavens, and were crowned with two fortresses flying the American flag.

As they drew closer to Michilimackinac, Henry saw how high it stood above the water. And he saw a town— their first since leaving Detroit. The town was built along the narrow plain below the hills and opened upon a deep harbor, which, Henry was certain, looked even busier than Detroit's. Not only was it checkered with ships at anchor, but from all points Indian canoes were moving in and out in such numbers that it would be hopeless even to try to count them.

Henry was happy to see Michilimackinac. So were the others. They had now traveled almost four hundred miles, most of it through wilderness country, with only water and sky for company. Moreover, their provisions had grown steadily lower as they approached Michili-mackinac. Here fresh provisions would be taken on. For the past ten days, the Ottawas and Shawnees of their party had gone to hunt for them at every camping place. They had brought in rabbits, water turtles, pigeons, and partridge. Sometimes they had caught fish to add to their meager rations. But now, once again, they could look forward to eating, without skimping on rations.

At Michilimackinac, as at Fort Gratiot, they were greeted by a salute from the garrison. A crowd of people, among them voyageurs who hoped to find friends in the party, had come down to meet them. They stood in a long line on shore. Indians had brought in word long before the expedition was near that they were on the way, and their movements had been reported day by day.

Governor Cass alone among the party seemed to be occupied with something other than their welcome. He was not even looking at the people gathered to meet them. His eyes were searching the harbor, and he seemed troubled.

"What's the matter, sir?" asked Major Forsyth.

"I don't see the ship with our provisions."

The Major looked around. "Perhaps they've come in, unloaded, and gone back."

"That's not likely."

So the provisions had not yet arrived! This would mean more delay for the expedition. Henry was not unhappy. Even though he knew the risks of delays, he wanted to talk to as many of the Indians and voyageurs as he could before they set out again. Besides, he told himself, it was only the sixth of June, and the weather, which had hardly had a chance to turn warm, would certainly not yet grow cold enough to freeze.

So, while they waited for the provisions to catch up, Henry moved about freely on the island. Sometimes Doty went with him. Henry enjoyed young Doty's company. Because Doty was so sure that he was destined to play a large part in the growth of the Michigan Territory he often acted as if he were already playing it. But Henry liked him as well as anyone in the party.

Most of the time, however, Parks went along so that

Henry could talk to the Indians, too. The two of them haunted the harbor. They went to the fur company offices. They talked to voyageurs and Indians. And always Henry asked—did they know where the great Father of Waters rose?

They received many answers, and often they were the same.

Again and again, Henry heard the voyageurs mention Lake La Biche. But from the descriptions they gave, Henry realized with sharp disappointment that those who said they had seen this lake were speaking of different bodies of water. At least three such different lakes were described. And all were called "La Biche."

Then, too, there were certain tantalizing hints. One grizzled voyageur and two Indians—Chippewas from far beyond the Sault de Ste. Marie—spoke of a blue jewel of water, hidden away in the hills and the forests. But they were vague and uncertain about where it was, save that it was far to the west, past the Fond du Lac at the end of Lake Superior.

One night during their stay at Michilimackinac, the party was entertained at dinner by Ramsay Crooks. Crooks was the master of the American Fur Company at Michilimackinac. He was a tall, shaggy man, with a shock of dark hair and large, prominent eyes looking out from under thick brows. He looked tired and bored but

Henry knew that this was a mask for Crooks' great shrewdness, of which he had heard.

When his eyes fell on Henry, Henry spoke. "Tell me, Mr. Crooks—what do you know about the headwaters of the Mississippi?"

"Very little. Only enough to be sure Pike was wrong," replied Crooks.

"Men from that region speak of a blue water deep in the hills."

Crooks laughed heartily. "My friend, this is a land of blue waters. All the waters of this country are as blue as the sky—except the Ontonagon River, which is a kind of brown because of copper and iron deposits which are said to be in that area."

"But this is a special one," said Henry earnestly. "They describe it as a blue jewel!"

Crooks shook his head tolerantly. "Do you know, Mr. Schoolcraft, in the western part of this Territory alone there are said to be as many as twelve thousand lakes. Perhaps there are more. And how many of them, do you think, might be called blue jewels? Thousands!"

Henry said no more. He was chastened and disappointed. All his inquiries had come to nothing.

*   *   *

Four days later the ship with the provisions came in.

It had been held back by the headwinds which had prevailed on Lake Huron.

With its arrival, a new problem arose. The region to the north and west of Michilimackinac to which they were traveling was one in which sudden storms and showers might occur at any time. And the corn, the flour, the bacon, and other supplies carried by the ship were not protected against such weather. A simple oilcloth cover would seldom be enough to keep the pelting rains and the often high waves of Lake Superior from spoiling some of the supplies. So they had to find enough ten-gallon kegs to hold all these provisions.

The preparation for the journey north took three more days.

Even then, there was a further interruption on the morning of the thirteenth, just as they were getting ready to start. While they were taking up their camp, Major Forsyth came out of the lifting fog.

"Governor Cass, sir—Lieutenant Pierce to see you."

"What the devil do they want now? Oh, well, send him on."

Lt. Pierce stepped briskly up. He saluted smartly. "I beg your pardon, sir, but the Captain has ordered twenty-one men under my command to lead the way to the Sault in a barge."

The Governor was astonished. "Lead the way!" he shouted in indignation. "Does he think I'm an Easterner?"

"No, sir. But certain friendly Indians have brought us information that some of the Chippewas of the Sault are very unfriendly to the United States. There have been threats that your party will never be permitted to pass through Lake Superior. As there isn't a garrison at the Sault, the best we can do in the circumstances, is to go along."

"Young man, I've been dealing with the Indians since before you were born," said the Governor testily.

"I'm sorry, sir. We have our orders."

Governor Cass shrugged and dismissed him. "This is what comes of Calhoun's sending word ahead to show us every courtesy. We're being coddled like babies—and I don't like it."

Major Forsyth smiled. He said nothing. He knew from long experience as the Governor's secretary how quickly the Governor's temper could be aroused—and how soon it could cool, if only no one argued with him.

In this case, no argument would help. The barge was already in place. The lifting fog showed twelve soldiers at the oars. Lt. Pierce was already on his way to take command of the vessel. The four canoes of the expedition were still along shore, though the Indians were moving out into the blue water of the lake. The voyageurs' canoe had an additional traveler, for Jean Roi, who worked for the American Fur Company and belonged to the post at the Fond du Lac, had joined them.

It was ten o'clock in the morning when the Governor's canoe left shore. The early fog had lifted before a rising wind. And the wind still blew strongly, at their backs.

This made the voyageurs happy, and they sang together in their strange patois. They sang with great gusto, knowing that a favorable wind would increase their speed. And they would need the wind's help if they hoped to reach the Sault in two days, for the Sault was a hundred miles away.

Before the day was out, they passed from Lake Huron into the straits of St. Mary. Here they lost the advantage of the wind, but they pressed on, led by the soldiers, who seemed determined that no one would ever say they had held up the speed of the expedition.

Soon the party was in the River St. Mary. Here they traveled in a region of many islands, moving along to the east of them. On the west side, where the water was deeper, the larger craft traveled. The water was so rapid and so shallow that one after another the canoes were injured. Little holes were torn into them by rocks they could not avoid. This continued to happen until there was nothing to do but repair the canoes, if they were to continue to travel.

This was Henry's first experience with the use of the things they had packed for just such accidents. The canoes were taken to shore, where the voyageurs and the

Indians worked together to unload them. Then a fire was built to heat the gum, and a few bundles of wattap were made ready to use.

The voyageurs were experts at repairing canoes. Once the unloading had been finished, they rapidly stripped the torn bark from the canoes, replaced it with new bark, and sewed and gummed it. In some places it was necessary only to put gum into the tears in the bark.

Two precious hours were lost in this way. As a result of this the Governor ordered the party forward through a drenching thunderstorm. Time lost must be made up whenever there was such a delay, he explained.

*　　*　　*

Late in the afternoon of their second day out from Michilimackinac, they came to the last and greatest of the rapids on the St. Mary. The village of the Sault lay just above, at the head of this last in a series of turbulent rapids which had challenged the voyageurs and Indians to do their best.

Here the St. Mary, a broad stream of white water, foamed over the rocks. There was no deeper channel on the far side of the river. This was as close as ships from the East could come to Lake Superior, though the long water of that lake lay only fifteen miles ahead. Here large vessels had to turn back, after their loads had been portaged to ships which waited above the rapids. Here,

in turn, they took on loads of furs portaged from ships
which plied Lake Superior and came east from the Fond
du Lac and the Northwest Passage.

The rapids stretched ahead for half a mile. The fall of
the river at this point was almost twenty-three feet. This
was a shallow and very treacherous piece of water. Governor Cass did not want to take any further chances with
the canoes, so he gave the signal to move in to shore.

There the soldiers, the Indians, and the voyageurs
unloaded some of the provisions from the canoes. These
were carried up along the shore to the village above.
Then the canoes, only half full now and much lighter,
were put in again, and driven sturdily through the dangerous water.

Shadow of Trouble

No CROWD OF PEOPLE had gathered to welcome them to
the village of the Sault. There were only two people along
the shore—a young man and a young woman. Governor
Cass knew them, for he waved to them well before the
canoes touched shore.

It was plain, too, from the way in which the Governor
embraced them when he landed, that they were old
friends. Doty, too, appeared to know them. The Governor drew Henry toward them.

"Schoolcraft, I want you to meet Jane Johnston and

her brother, George," he said. "They are the children of my old friend, John Johnston, who is surely the most important man of the Sault."

Henry shook hands gravely with each of them. He was immediately favorably impressed by Jane. He thought her a very attractive girl. She did not look much like the Eastern girls he had known. They were so white that they were almost without color. Jane, on the other hand, was deeply tanned. Her face was long and oval, and out of it shone two very dark eyes. Her hair, which was drawn straight back and parted in the middle, was dark too.

"Since Father has gone to Europe," Jane said to the Governor, "we've come to offer you our home during your visit here, Mr. Cass."

"Anyone who has once known the hospitality of the Johnston home could never afterward refuse it," said the Governor gallantly.

Jane Johnston blushed prettily at his compliment.

"But we're prepared to encamp just outside your house, Miss Johnston," the Governor went on. "And, since we're fully equipped, we shouldn't disturb your arrangements."

"Our father would wish you to stay with us, Mr. Cass," said Jane in a pleasing voice. "And we, too, hope you'll make our house your own."

Governor Cass thanked her and offered her his arm on

the way back to where the Johnston house stood on a
rise at the far edge of the settlement.

Parks came up behind Henry and Doty.

"Their mother was Chippewa, daughter of old Chief
Waubjeeg," explained Parks, seeing the direction of
Henry's glance. "She died."

"An Indian?" asked Henry, startled.

Doty smiled. "Many of the early traders married Indian girls, Schoolcraft," he said. "And lived quite happily, too. Why should they not?"

For this, Henry had no answer. He had not yet taken
his eyes from Jane. She was as comely a young lady as he
had ever met, and very different from other young
women he had known. Perhaps this was because she was
half Indian.

Now, as the Governor and Jane and her brother
walked ahead, Henry looked around at the settlement.
The village of the Sault was unlike those of Detroit and
Michilimackinac. Detroit was a young city. Michilimackinac was a bustling, growing, and very clean town. But
the Sault de Ste. Marie looked like a very old village indeed. Of its twenty houses, at least half showed signs of
age and wear. A few of them were actually falling together. There were some signs of ruins. These had once
been a fort and barracks, but there was no fort at the
Sault now. Before one could be put up again, the government would have to have the permission of the Chip-

pewas. And the government would need to buy the land from these Indians; that was one of the Governor's main reasons for visiting the Sault.

Not far back from the village itself stood a large number of Chippewa lodges, more than Henry had ever seen before. He counted almost forty of them, all of good size, and well-built. This indicated that the Indians lived there permanently.

"Are these Indians warlike?" Henry asked.

Parks shrugged. "They are not like other Chippewas. We call them the Saulteurs. Might be two hundred live here. They can fight, but they are great fishermen. They live on whitefish."

"It must be monotonous to eat fish all the time."

Parks laughed heartily, as if Henry had made a joke. "Oh, they sell them, too. Come—you see."

Parks led the way toward the deep water which lay above the rapids. Here was a large pier which stuck out from an island off shore, making a harbor of good size. A schooner from the northwest lay in it, waiting for goods to be portaged from ships on the other side of the rapids. Not far away, close to the shore, were five or six light canoes, each with two Indians in it.

"See," said Parks. "One steers, the other fishes from the prow. They go from rock to rock. Look how clear the water is, an' how many whitefish there are in it. The Indians can see far down."

The Chippewas were swift and sure of themselves. The steersman never had to turn to see what his companion was doing. He could tell by the movements in the canoe just what the other was about. The fisherman did not use anything but a long pole with a net on one end. Each time the canoe passed over a school of whitefish, he dipped his net far down into the water among the fish crowded below. Each time he brought up his catch to dump it into the canoe. Henry did not see a net come up less than half full. Some of the nets were so full that fish fell back into the water over the rims as they were drawn up into the canoes.

"They can take maybe five hundred in two hours," said Parks.

"What do they do with so many?" asked Doty.

"Ah, they are smart, these Saulterurs. They clean an' cure them. Then they dry them in smoke, so they can keep them as long as they like to eat or to sell. You will see. They taste better than Mackinac trout." He turned away. "Come. Now we catch up with the others."

"These Indians are enterprising," observed Doty to Henry.

Henry was thinking the same thing. These Indians were not standing around waiting for gifts from the white men.

Up ahead of them, the other members of the expedi-

tion had halted in a hard little group. Seeing this, Parks quickened his steps. He looked worried.

"That is the Johnston house," Parks said, pointing to a dwelling well beyond the place where the party stood. He went right on speaking, as his eyes sought out the portly figure of the Governor. "Maybe we make a mistake to go back. Some of these Saulteurs are great friends with the British. They do not like Americans. Yes, there is Sassaba—they call him the Count."

"Who is he?" asked Henry.

Doty replied. "He is the chief of those Chippewas who seem to prefer the British."

"See how he stand with his arms folded!" whispered Parks, excitedly.

Sassaba was tall for an Indian. He stood with his arms folded across his chest, facing the Governor, a wooden expression on his face. He was dressed in tribal costume, befitting his rank, and looked very fierce and arrogant.

Parks was a little in the lead when the three of them came up. They were just in time to hear the last of the talk between Sassaba and the Governor. Though Parks had not been there to translate, and neither had Riley, both the Johnstons could speak the language of the Chippewas.

His braves stood on either side of the Count, and behind him. They looked just as fierce as he. The Governor was flanked by Trowbridge and Douglass. Jane and

George Johnston were speaking angrily to the chieftain.

Parks listened for a moment and translated for Henry and Doty. "Sassaba has not shake hands with the Governor. They tell him he must do so." He shook his head ominously. "There may be trouble. Sassaba, he has no like for Americans, an' he make a bid for control of all the Chippewas here at the Sault. That will be very bad for the Americans."

Henry's eyes strayed to Jane Johnston, just as she stepped back, her face flushed with anger. He thought she looked prettier than ever. Her brother stood his ground; he was ummoved by Sassaba's defiance. Henry wondered why Jane had stepped back; he resolved to ask her.

Neither Sassaba nor the Governor would retreat an inch. All the braves waited to see what Sassaba would do. If he gave way, then so would they. If he did not, then neither would they.

Suddenly George Johnston stepped closer to Sassaba and said something urgently to him. He spoke with an air of menace. Then slowly, grudgingly, Sassaba put out his hand and took the Governor's. For the moment, the crisis was past. Sassaba looked sulkily away and stepped back after he had shaken hands with Governor Cass.

The Governor's party went on toward the Johnston house.

This was perhaps the largest building in Sault de Ste.

Marie. It was also one of the oldest. John Johnston, said Doty, as they walked along, had come to live at the Sault soon after the first war with England, the Revolution, had ended. He had lived there ever since, though he had traveled widely into the wilderness and back to the older countries. Though the house was large enough to accommodate them all, the Governor was not to be moved from his position that his camp should be separate from the house, no matter how close it might be.

Yet for this evening there was no help for it, they must take supper with the Johnstons. Their hosts had prepared for them. It would be needlessly impolite to refuse to do so. So, leaving the camp to be set up by the voyageurs and the Indians, the members of the expedition retired to the house.

There Henry quickly forgot about the Indians and the shadow of trouble which now lay over the party because of Sassaba's attitude against the Americans. He was fascinated by Jane Johnston and could hardly take his eyes from her. How skillful and capable she was! How well ordered the house in which they were guests! Now for a little while, he would be able to forget that they were in wild country, and going to wilder. For here, in this house, there were all the comforts of the civilization they had left behind them.

*   *   *

After supper, Henry lingered until at last only he and the Governor of all the expedition were left in the house, with their hosts. The Governor was talking with George Johnston about a council of the Indian chiefs he planned to call. Thus Henry found himself alone with Jane.

"Tell me, Miss Johnston," he said. "I am curious—this afternoon when you were talking with Sassaba, you seemed to give up and step back. Why?"

"Indian men are very proud. They would never want to seem to give way to a woman," she answered. "So I stepped back and left George alone with him. In that way he would not lose face before his chiefs."

"What is that—'lose face'?"

"Why, it means that he would be belittled in his own and their estimation." She looked curiously at him out of her soft dark eyes. "You do not know very much about the Indians, Mr. Schoolcraft?"

"No, I'm from the East."

"And perhaps you too think of them only as barbarians, perhaps even savages?"

Henry smiled ruefully. "I confess I had some ideas which I can see now were quite wrong."

Her voice grew more gentle. "My mother was an Indian, Mr. Schoolcraft. She was a very fine woman." She spoke with warm pride.

"I'm sure she was," said Henry. "She could not have been your mother had she been otherwise."

Jane looked at him gravely for a moment. Then she said, "Thank you, Mr. Schoolcraft."

"I came along on this expedition as a geologist, Miss Johnston," Henry said earnestly. "But I find myself more and more interested in the Indians, and less in rocks and stones."

"I hope that interest will continue, Mr. Schoolcraft. The Indians need an interpreter who has understanding and sympathy. They need someone who will look at them as fellow human beings, and not just as curiosities. The Indians are a very proud people, and they have lived for many hundreds of years by a code as strict as any ever devised by white men."

"And Sassaba?"

"He is only one of many chiefs who have become dissatisfied. The Indians have been betrayed many times by the greed of white men, Mr. Schoolcraft. Being aware of this, Sassaba is easily misled."

"You think he is right, Miss Johnston?"

"No, Mr. Schoolcraft. But certain British traders are always interested in stirring up trouble with the Americans, for if the Indians dislike the Americans, and refuse land for a fort, then the British fur trade will be so much better. The Indians will bring their furs to them instead. So the British make presents to the chiefs. They flatter them, and make many promises they do not intend to keep. And because the chiefs are just as human as the rest of us, they want to believe that they have friends who will stand with them against the Americans."

"I understand." And indeed, he did understand how the Indians must resent the invasion of land which had been theirs for centuries, by strange white men, and how they would welcome any allies. "And do you believe, too, that there should not be a garrison here?"

Jane shook her head. "No, Mr. Schoolcraft. I believe a garrison ought to be established here once more. The Chippewas know it cannot be stopped, but Sassaba is showing that he would like to stop it. All the Indians know, Mr. Schoolcraft, that the white men come like a tide, again and again. They cannot stop them. They can only hope to find among them men who are as honest as themselves, who never break their word, as the Indian does not."

Her eyes softened again, and she added, "My mother used to say that the Indians are like the leaves of a tree in the Moon of Falling Leaves driving before the wind, that is the coming of the white man."

"How well said that is, Miss Johnston."

Her smile came suddenly. "I think you would have liked my mother, Mr. Schoolcraft."

Governor Cass came to his feet suddenly and looked to where Henry sat with Jane.

"Come, Schoolcraft—the night is half gone. It's time for honest folk to be abed."

Henry came to his feet with alacrity. He had not realized that time had passed so swiftly. It was a tribute to Jane that he had never been aware of the passage of a moment in her company.

The Medicine Dance

EARLY IN THE AFTERNOON of the next day, the Governor
interrupted another conversation Henry was having with
Jane Johnston. He came into the house where the two sat
talking.

"I think you may want to come along, Schoolcraft,"
he said. "We've had an invitation to watch one of the
Chippewa ceremonies—the Grand Medicine Dance."

Henry looked toward Jane. "I'd rather stay here, sir."

"I think you ought to go, Mr. Schoolcraft," said Jane.
"Will you go, too?"

"If Governor Cass will invite me," Jane answered quietly.

"I do indeed," said the Governor hastily. "We should be honored by your company, Miss Johnston."

"What does the ceremony mean?" asked Henry.

"The Indians have a little group of Medicine Men," explained Jane. "It's almost a kind of special society to them. They call themselves the Grand Medicines. It is considered an honor to watch the ritual, which is given to celebrate the admission of a new member to the circle."

"I'm afraid, though, this invitation has another motive behind it," said the Governor. "Sassaba had a hand in sending it. I know he doesn't mean us well."

"Are we to expect trouble, sir?" asked Henry.

"Not at the medicine dance, no. Sassaba is more bluster than action. But he will try to impress the other chiefs. No, I think trouble may come at tomorrow's council."

"Why go, then, sir?"

The Governor shook his head. "I couldn't refuse. The rest of you needn't come, if you'd rather not. But if I were to refuse, it would seem to them a profound insult. It might endanger the success of the council."

The ceremony was held in a large wigwam. Henry had never seen one so large. It was uncovered at the top. On the poles which stuck out above the walls, bits of blankets and other materials were hanging. Henry thought some of them were scalps.

"What are they?" he asked Jane.

"They are offerings to Manitou," she answered softly.

All around the wigwam, inside, sat Indian men and squaws, though most of the watchers were men. The majority of the squaws belonging to the men who took part, were collected outside. All the watchers were covered with ornaments of many kinds, and each one was painted so that it was almost impossible to tell whether they had been met before.

All but one—that was Sassaba. He was resplendent, not in Indian garb, except for his headdress, but in the coat of a British uniform, with two epaulettes. He was the picture of insolent pride. Governor Cass pretended not to notice him at all. When Jane saw him, she bit her lower lip as if she were hurt.

As soon as the members of the expedition were there, the ceremony began. In the center of the wigwam were two old men who held a long drum. One of them beat on the drum, and the other shook a gourd shell rattle, keeping time with the drummer. Next to them, between them and the circle of Indians squatting on their haunches, were eight dancers. These dancers moved around the musicians with a solemn, measured step. Most of the time they went very slowly, but every little while they almost ran. But, slow or fast, they always kept in step.

The watching braves and squaws around the inner wall

of the wigwam kept time, too. They nodded their heads or moved their hands together soundlessly. But now and then they made a strange, low, moaning undertone. As he listened, Henry realized that the moaning was really always present. Sometimes it sank so low as to be almost unheard; then again it swelled out strongly. At the same time, the gourd rattler kept up a kind of chant.

All those taking part in the dance held a dressed animal skin in one hand. These skins were of all kinds—otter, martin, beaver, weasel. Now and then one of the dancers cried out sharply in imitation of the voice of the animal whose skin he carried. This imitation was so good that the first time Henry heard it he looked hastily around for the animal which he thought had cried. Every time this cry was given, the players and the dancers went faster. They redoubled their motions, and their eyes strained so that they seemed about to burst from their sockets.

Jane whispered at Henry's side. "The dancers are the Medicine Men, Mr. Schoolcraft. They are powerful members of the tribe. In all the councils only the chiefs can prevail against them. If you'll watch closely, you'll see how the Medicine Men signify their power. Every motion they make has a meaning."

"Are they old men or young, Miss Johnston? I can't tell, for the paint."

"Most of them are older men."

Suddenly the Medicine Men did something different.

One at a time, each Medicine Man lifted the animal skin he carried. He breathed into the mouth at the end of the skin. Then he chose someone from among the old men and squaws who watched. He pointed the mouth of the skin at whomever he had chosen, with a quick thrusting motion. There seemed to be a little snapping noise whenever this was done. What looked like a white bean appeared to shoot out of the dead mouth and strike the Indian at whom the skin was pointed.

Then a very strange thing happened. The Indian so struck fell to the earth and lay there motionless, as if he had been stunned. He lay as long as two minutes. Then he struggled back up again, but with what looked like a great deal of difficulty. He worked so hard to sit up again that he made it look as if a spell had been put on him by the dancing Medicine Man.

This happened quite often. Sometimes one Medicine Man cast his spell. Sometimes all were doing it at the same time. Now and then half the circle of watchers were prostrated at the same time. But this was all part of the ritual of the Grand Medicine Dance.

Henry could hardly take his eyes from it. He figured out, with Jane's promptings, that the breathing into the mouth of the dead skin, followed by the pointing of the skin at chosen watchers, was a way of showing everyone present how powerful the Medicine Men were.

He guessed, too, that the Indians who sat along the

wall were also Medicine Men, because they changed places with the dancers. Sometimes one of the dancers grew tired. Then he moved toward the wall of the wigwam, out of the dancing circle. Immediately another old man jumped up and entered into the dance. The tired dancer sat down in his place.

Soon all those who had begun the dance were sitting down and others were carrying on. Sometimes there were as many as a dozen dancers. The number did not remain the same. It depended on how much room there was and on how the old man felt about dancing. Once in a while there were so many Indians moving back and forth that it was almost impossible to see the drummer and the gourd rattler.

The musicians changed almost as often as the dancers. Those who took their places had to wait until the drum or the gourd was offered to them. It was clear to Henry that all those who took part, watching or dancing or playing, were trained to play any role in the ceremony. There was nothing to show which one was the new member. All were equal. The new member must have been trained before the ceremony of initiation.

At the height of the ceremony, everyone was crying out or moaning. The painted faces were twisted and open-mouthed. The Chippewas looked just as the Easterners pictured them most of the time—like weird, painted devils! If he had not known what the ceremony was about, Henry might easily have become alarmed, so fierce did the Indians look!

Jane touched his arm gently. Henry turned and met her smile. "You are like an excited boy, Mr. Schoolcraft!" she whispered.

"I *am* excited," he answered. "This is very impressive. I will never forget it. I'm not quite sure what it all means, but I'll find out."

"It is all meant to show that the Medicine Man is the all powerful man of his tribe—next to the chiefs. He is the priest and the doctor," explained Jane.

"But surely he knows no medicine, Miss Johnston!"

"Many Indians are wise in the ways of healing, Mr. Schoolcraft. Remember, they have studied the healing magic of leaves and roots and flowers and seeds for many, many hundreds of years. It is the Medicine Man who knows all about healing. He has had handed down to him the power of herbs to help the sick. He brews the medicines and cares for those who are ill."

"But does he ever cure the sick?"

"I have seen the Medicine Man cure the sick, Mr. Schoolcraft," Jane answered, soberly.

Henry could not doubt her. She spoke with respect.

"Then," she went on, "it is the Medicine Man who knows the dances which will drive out devils. Many Indians believe that sickness is a devil which takes possession of the body."

"There are white civilizations which also believe that," admitted Henry.

"Only the chief of all the tribes is held to be more powerful than the Medicine Man, and his power isn't to cure, but to rule," finished Jane.

"Do they come in conflict with each other?"

"They try to avoid any appearance of conflict, Mr. Schoolcraft."

At last the ceremony ended, and the Indians waited for their guests to take their leave.

Governor Cass rose instantly. Without saying a word to anyone, not even to the members of his party, he strode away in silent dignity.

Parks nudged Henry. "You see," he said. "He was insulted!"

"But no one paid any attention to him," protested Henry. "How could he have been insulted. He's not a vain man." He flashed a glance at Jane and saw by the expression of her face that she, too, knew that Governor Cass had been insulted.

Parks wagged his head. "You do not see?" He turned and pointed to the Indians leaving the ceremonial wigwam. He singled out Sassaba. "See there. Sassaba wear a British soldier's coat. He do so on purpose. Now, then, my frien', to ask the American Governor to come, an' then to come himself in a British soldier's coat—that is to insult the Governor!"

Henry understood. Sassaba had deliberately put on this uniform to show the Governor that his sympathies were with the British, that he was hostile to the United States and any plans that the United States might have for the Chippewas of the Sault. Yet Sassaba and his people lived on American land, and traded with the American traders.

Henry looked to Jane.

She nodded. "I'm afraid what Mr. Parks says is true, Mr. Schoolcraft. Try not to judge him too harshly. Sassaba is a simple and unwise man. He should not have done this."

"You see. There will be trouble," prophesied Parks.

"I hope not," said Jane earnestly.

"Do you mean war, Parks?" asked Henry.

Parks shrugged and spread his hands. "Who is it will say? Not if the Governor can stop it. We will see tomorrow who is the stronger one—the Governor or Sassaba. All the Indians—they much respec' the stronger. I bet on the Governor. I know him. Jus' the same, the soldiers who came with Lt. Pierce—they are spoiling for a fight. I do not like soldiers; they like too much to play with guns."

The Council at the Sault

THE NEXT DAY was the day of the council.

Governor Cass had sent word by runners to all the chiefs of the Chippewa tribes, those who lived farther inland as well as those who lived at the Sault. Half the night the voyageurs and Indians of the Governor's party had worked under his supervision to prepare a suitable marquee for the Governor.

The marquee was a kind of walled canopy extending out from the Governor's tent. Governor Cass was to sit in the middle of it and look as much like a king as possible. As far as he was concerned, the Governor would just as soon have squatted down, Indian fashion, on the grass. But then the Indians might not have thought of him as a leader. So he had to sit in his marquee, on a little raised platform made of three logs clamped together, and covered with boards and a mat. George Johnston had taken an armchair from his father's house for the Governor to sit upon.

The chiefs began to come in early in the morning. Each of them came with a large party. It looked as if each chieftain had brought along his pick of his braves, just in case there was any trouble.

The Governor matched this act. He ordered all the soldiers of the party, together with Lt. Pierce and his men, to line up behind and beside the marquee, where their blue uniforms would look most impressive.

The marquee had been put up in an open place just outside the village. Each chief, as he came in, had his wigwam pitched at a respectful distance from the marquee, but facing it. They knew that the council would take place before the marquee. Soon there was a semi-circle of wigwams facing the marquee. And squarely in the center of that semi-circle was the large, colorful wigwam of Chief Sassaba.

When the Governor received word that all the chiefs he had sent for were there, he left the Johnston house and walked to the marquee with the members of his party. He knew very well that the Indians were aware of the reason for the council. They knew that the United States was now ready to claim the treaty rights which the Indians had once ceded to the French and the English. These rights had come down to the Americans, now that the French and British no longer ruled the land, because when General Wayne had signed the treaty of Greenville twenty-five years before, he had signed a saving clause for the land. Because the French and the British had had the right to a military post at the Sault, so did the Americans.

Up to this time, the Americans had not wanted to erect a post at the Sault. But ever since the War of 1812, the traders and the military men along the frontier had urged the Secretary of War to establish a garrison there. The Governor was aware that the Chippewas knew this. Word of it had been sent to them by the British, who had found it out. The British were worried that the Americans might make war on them again. Besides, the British just across the Sault, wanted to keep the Chippewas more free to bring their furs to them.

The exact purpose of the council was to settle with the Indians the boundaries of the grant of land from the Indians to the United States.

As the Governor now walked toward his marquee, the Indians began to come from their wigwams. They took their places in a half-circle before the Governor's tent. Each of the chiefs was dressed in his best. They wore a great many different costumes, but all wore many beaded pieces of clothing. The beads were made of colored porcupine quills. Some wore headdresses. Some wore only a few tall feathers in bands around their heads. None wore paint except Sassaba, who had a bright splash of yellow on one cheek. He alone was not in Indian dress. Once more he wore the insulting British uniform. In this red coat he stood out among all the others, even though all the chiefs were colorful.

The Governor, having reached the marquee, turned to the Indians, held up one hand in the traditional gesture of friendship, and began to speak. Beside him, Parks translated into the Chippewa language.

"My children," the Governor said, "the Great White Father sends you his greetings." So he began.

All the chiefs sat listening without moving a muscle.

The Governor went on to review the history of the treaties. Had not the Chippewas given right to land for a military post to the French? To the British? Indeed they had. Had not this right come down to the Americans? It was so. All that remained to be done was to mark out the boundaries of the grant, so that the Americans could build their fort upon it and bring the soldiers to live there.

As soon as they had finished, the chiefs began to speak. They spoke one at a time. Each rose with great ceremony and said what he thought. They spoke very simply, but very effectively.

Henry listened closely to the translations as Parks made them. One after another, the Chippewa chiefs pretended to know nothing of the treaty which had given the Americans the rights the Governor claimed. They affected ignorance of any such grant for a military purpose.

In reply, the Governor patiently cited the time and the place of the treaty. He named the signatures put to it, Indian as well as white.

Finally one old chief rose and signaled for attention among the rising melee of Indian voices.

"Let Grey Cloud speak," commanded the Governor.

The old chieftain spoke. "The Great White Father makes many promises. He does not always keep them. Some of us know of the treaty. Some do not. Some of us are not afraid to settle the boundary as the White Father asks. But we would settle it only if it is not occupied by the soldiers.

"We do not wish the white soldiers to come. They are strict. They carry guns. They use these guns against our people. It has been known that our young men become unruly. They are restless. They are filled with wild, young blood. They want to take meat in the custom of their ancestors. But taking meat is now forbidden by the Great White Father. So, if our young men become unruly, they might take their guns and kill the dogs or the cows which stray away from the fort. Then there is no telling what will happen. But the night wind says there will be no peace."

Grey Cloud sat down, cross-legged. Everyone waited for the Governor to reply. What old Grey Cloud had said was a kind of threat. Everyone understood it to be so, even the members of the Governor's party who were close enough to hear Parks' translation.

The Governor came to his feet and held up his hand for silence.

"My children," he said again. "Whether you set the boundary or whether you do not set it—no matter. Be not uneasy. Be not afraid, as we are not. As surely as there is the sun in the sky—" Here he pointed to the sun. "—so there will be soldiers at the Sault. You cannot stop their coming. I cannot stop it. If the Great White Father wills it, it will be so."

He sat down again.

When Parks had finished translating this speech, there was great excitement among the Indians. They were impressed by the Governor's firmness. They knew that if Cass spoke in this fashion, then it was the truth. They had been told that the Americans did not want to put a fort there. They had been told other tales of someone's invention. They had been misinformed. Still, they did not know what to do.

One among them cried out suddenly, "Let Sassaba be heard!"

Henry looked quickly toward the central wigwam. Sassaba had come prepared to set his people against the Governor, and that success depended on how much better he could present his case than the Governor had presented the government's. Would Sassaba now defy the Governor?

Slowly Sassaba got to his feet. He took his war lance and stuck it savagely into the ground before him. His expression was wild and warlike. His very appearance and manner excited the other chiefs and the young braves so much more. A quick ripple of alarm went through the Governor's party, for the soldiers were outnumbered by four to one.

The other Chippewa chiefs, who had been speaking urgently and with many gestures among themselves, fell silent. They waited on Sassaba's words. Not all of them, as Henry could see by the way in which they looked at the Count, approved of him. Yet they were willing to listen to what he said. They wanted to see how the Governor would react to it.

Now that Henry looked from one to another of the chiefs, he saw for the first time that many of them wore epaulettes and ornaments which could only have come from the British across the Sault in Canada. The Chippewas had undoubtedly put them on to make the Ameri-

cans understand how much their sympathies were with their British friends.

Sassaba began to speak and silence fell.

"We are Chippewa," he said. "We shall remain Chippewa. We shall not be told by the Great White Father how to give away our land. What manner of men are these white brothers who hope to come here? We know their kind. They will come with silken smiles and golden promises. Their words will be as honey, but their deeds will be as gall. When we have been lulled to peace, they will make war upon us. They will kill our braves, our women, our children. They have done so before. They will do it again. This land is ours. We will not part with it. Those who signed such a treaty were not speaking for us. So be it."

Having spoken, Sassaba seized his war lance and pulled it from the ground. Then he turned to the presents which had been brought for the chiefs and rudely kicked at them. They scattered to all sides.

The Governor sat where he was, without moving. His face was set with anger. He made no attempt to speak, though Parks waited on him to do so.

The chiefs and the braves, as well as the Indian women and children, were greatly excited. There was a welling up of talk, and again, many gestures were exchanged among the Indians. Some of the Chippewas seemed to approve Sassaba's defiance; others disapproved.

Sassaba, having spurned the Governor and his gifts, turned his back on him. He stalked away to his wigwam. Then, one by one, the other chiefs retreated from the council and went to their wigwams.

Seeing this, the Governor rose and walked away from his marquee, going toward the tents set up near the Johnston house.

For the moment, the rest of the party lingered. Henry and Captain Douglass, as well as Doty, were especially anxious to see what would take place next. What would the Chippewas do? Behind them, Lt. Pierce and the troops were chattering excitedly. Some of the soldiers were sure there would be war. They were resolving to sell their lives as dearly as possible.

Parks alone did not seem troubled. "Sassaba—he is a bad one," he said, as he came over to where they stood. He was grinning. "But much wind, much face. Watch an' see."

"Seems to me it's the Governor's move," said Doty.

"But what can he do, short of threatening them with arms?" asked Henry.

Douglass interrupted him, grabbing him by the arm. "Will you look at that!" he cried, pointing.

There, floating above Sassaba's tent, was the British flag.

"Now the Governor mus' do somet'ing," said Parks. "But who will tell him?"

"I will," said Douglass. "I'll tell him right now."

He began to run toward the Johnston house. This was down the hill from the place of the council.

At the sight of Douglass coming on the run, the voyageurs and Indians, as well as those members of the party who had not come to the council, came from their tents. Douglass ran straight into the Johnston house, which the Governor had entered with George Johnston.

Less than a minute passed by.

Then the Governor came stalking from the house. He retraced his steps with purpose in his stride. He came up the hill in long steps. Parks ran a little to keep up with him. Henry joined Douglass and followed. At this moment, so much was Henry impressed by the cloud of rage on the Governor's heavy face, that he forgot his alarm at the unfriendliness of the Chippewas.

The Governor went straight into Sassaba's wigwam. The British flag jerked and trembled. Then it came down. The Governor had pulled it down, and now he brought it out of the wigwam. There, before all the Indians who had assembled at sight of his coming, he threw it to the ground and trampled on it. In this way he showed his contempt of Sassaba's action. Then he turned to Sassaba and openly sneered at him.

Sassaba was so surprised that he did not know how to reply. This time it was the Governor who did not give his opponent a chance to answer. He beckoned Parks close and began to speak in a voice that trembled with fury.

"Mark me well, my children," he said. "The Great White Father will not accept such an insult as this. No flag flies in the land of the Great White Father but the flag of the United States. Hear me! If one among you dares again to raise a foreign flag over the land of the Great White Father, I will order the soldiers to fire on you, and to fire until all are slain. I will seize your land and I will hunt you down and banish you from the land of your ancestors until all are gone."

Then he bent and snatched up the flag. He walked away, dragging it behind him.

The Chippewas who had witnessed what he did and had heard him speak through Parks, were badly upset. For a few moments no one spoke. Not a voice was raised. Then one of the chiefs suddenly tore off his British medal and threw it to the ground. Another followed his example. Soon all were talking at once in a state of great excitement.

All this time Sassaba had not said a word. He did not know what to say. He thought he had carried the day with his bold speech defying the Governor and the Great White Father. Now he saw that it was not so. He had gone too far when he had raised the British flag. Now he realized that the Governor was ready to go to war. He knew, too, that the British would not help the Chippewas, for it had happened in this way before. He turned and went into his wigwam when the other chiefs began to shout at him in anger.

The whole Indian encampment was now in turbulent motion. No one paid any attention to Henry or Douglass or Doty. Henry watched with an interest all the more keen since he could not but feel a lurking sympathy for the Indians. He had already come a far way from his preconceived notion of what Indians were like.

As he watched, Henry saw that there was a definite pattern to the movements of the Chippewas. The women and the children, together with all the old men who held no rank, were moving toward the river. There they began to enter the canoes to go to the other side.

"They're afraid of war," said Doty. "See, they're moving those who can't fight."

At the same time, the chiefs continued to discard all their British ornaments. Some of the warriors who had surrounded Sassaba, began to look in anger toward the three members of the Governor's party who still remained, so, to avoid an incident which might lead to trouble, they walked away.

The Governor had retired to his tent. He was talking with Dr. Wolcott when Henry came in with Doty and Douglass.

"What are they doing?" asked Wolcott. "Do they mean to fight?"

"They are certainly preparing for a battle," said Douglass.

Henry described what they had seen. When he told how the chiefs were tearing off their British decorations, Governor Cass smiled.

"They're learning how they were misled," he said. "There'll be no battle. Unless Sassaba fights alone, and I doubt that he will. He is no coward; but he has now lost face badly and he'll find no one ready to follow him."

They sat waiting on events, talking over the council and Sassaba's bold challenge. It was clear to Henry that, no matter how much Governor Cass had disapproved Sassaba's defiance, he had a kind of admiration for him for having made the attempt. But he would probably never admit it, Henry thought.

Less than half an hour passed. Then, suddenly, George Johnston appeared at the tent's opening.

"Governor, several of the Chippewa chiefs are at our house," he said. "They're anxious to talk with you. They don't agree with Sassaba."

"They have lost no time," said Governor Cass tranquilly. "I'll talk to them at once, before Sassaba can stir up more trouble."

Johnston turned, saying, "I'll tell them."

"No, George—I'll go to them. They have come thus far to see me. Now it is my turn to go a little way."

The chiefs who were waiting for Governor Cass numbered at least a dozen. This was more than half the total number of Chippewa leaders at the council. No sooner had the Governor appeared than their spokesman, who was old Grey Cloud, offered his apologies to the Governor. He apologized in the name of all the chieftains for the conduct of Sassaba.

"Sassaba does not speak for us," old Grey Cloud said. "Sassaba is young. He is not led by his head but by his heart."

"Sassaba had a right to speak as he did," said Governor Cass. "But he had no right to raise the British flag."

"We did not tell him to do so. The redcoats have spoken to Sassaba's heart. See, we have torn away all the things the British have given us. We no longer listen to these voices from the north."

Indeed, all the chiefs were dressed differently from the way they had been dressed for the council. They were more dignified because they were so plainly dressed. They still wore their colorful beads, but their headdresses were subdued. Those who had worn broadcloth coats had discarded them. Now they sat half-naked, with the light gleaming on their bronze skin. To Henry, they seemed to have a kind of nobility which was a part of their resignation to the Governor's will.

"Our people do not want war," Grey Cloud went on.

"We, who lead them, know the might of the Great White Father and his armies. Say to us, will you talk over this matter with us?"

"We will talk of it now," agreed the Governor.

"The soldiers will not fire on our people?"

"They will not. I have not given the order to fire. I will not do so unless the Great White Father is insulted again as he was by Sassaba," answered the Governor.

He was so clearly sincere, that their relief showed on their faces. They grew less anxious. It began to seem to them not only that they had less reason to worry, but that they might hope for some concessions from the Governor. They had come prepared to agree to all the Governor's demands, but now perhaps they need not surrender everything.

"If we grant you this land within the boundaries you ask," continued Grey Cloud, "what of the fishing at the falls?"

"These rights are yours for all time. The Great White Father wants nothing but the land for the fort, so that the soldiers may have a place to live."

"Must we then camp away from the shore?"

"You may camp on the shore."

This pleased them all. It meant that they surrendered nothing but land they did not use in any case. The building of a fort would not disturb their fishing. They could still camp where they liked, close to the fishing grounds.

Nothing would change in their way of life, which was a happy one and pleased them.

"We will come back," promised Grey Cloud. "We will not talk about this with Sassaba."

*   *   *

In late afternoon, almost all the Chippewa chiefs were back. Sassaba was not with them. Now they were ready to sign the treaty which the Governor had had prepared. It called for ceding to the United States a tract of land four miles square. This tract commenced at the Sault and extended two miles up and two miles down the river. It included the portage and the sites of the village and the old fort. In the treaty, too, the express rights of the Chippewas to fish and camp at the places where they had always done so were set down.

Governor Cass read the agreement aloud, and Parks translated it to the chiefs. As each point was read, they grunted and nodded in approval. When their own rights were read to them, they looked at one another with triumph, just as if they had won an important victory, after all. And without Sassaba, or a shot fired on either side.

Now the women and children could come back to the wigwams. All would be as before.

The old chiefs were eager to sign.

Having done so, they produced the pipe of peace. Grey Cloud took a puff from it and passed it to the other chiefs. They in turn handed it to the Governor, who took a long, deep pull of it. Then the handshaking began. Everybody shook hands with everybody else. The Chippewas seemed to enjoy this as much as one of their tribal rituals. They shook hands again and again until the Governor signaled for silence and attention.

The Chippewas knew what this meant. Now was the time for their gifts.

The same presents which had been spurned earlier in the day by Sassaba were now brought forward. They consisted of knives, blankets, silverware, broadcloth, and other goods which the Indians coveted. Henry watched their pleasure with some curiosity. It seemed to him that if they treasured the goods of white men, they wished perhaps to be in part like the white men.

The Governor held up his hand for silence, and the old chiefs stood by respectfully to listen.

"There is no present for Sassaba," said the Governor. "But say to him that the White Father has forgiven his rash act. Say to him that it is better to be friends with the Great White Father than to live in anger with him. Say to him that in his heart the White Father understands him, but that by the law of the Great White Father, which both of us must obey, he cannot tolerate his allegiance to another power. Say to him that if he prefers the British, he is free to cross the river and live among them. He is free to go. We will not stop him. But say to him also that we look with pleasure on his bravery and courage, and we would be honored if he chose to stay among us."

This speech pleased the chiefs as much as the gifts. They shook hands all around again and took their departure, proudly carrying their gifts.

"I could not help feeling that that was a magnanimous gesture, sir," said Henry.

"The message to Sassaba?" The Governor shook his head. "No, Schoolcraft. Magnanimity has little to do with it. If Sassaba hadn't done what he did, we'd still be parleying. We are now free to go on. On the other hand, how unwise it is to leave enemies at one's back! Sassaba will now get back a little of his face, but none of his power."

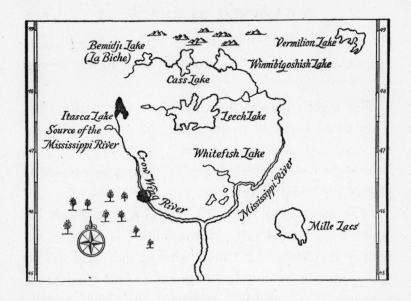

Into the West

THE MORNING OF DEPARTURE was one of excited haste. All were eager to go ahead, though Henry was not quite as anxious. He had grown so fond of Jane Johnston in this short visit, that he would like to have stayed longer. Yet he would not have remained behind for anything. Nevertheless, having packed, he took time to go to the Johnston house and make his private farewells to Jane.

It seemed to him that she had been waiting for him to come. But perhaps that was what he wished to think.

"I came to say good-by, Miss Johnston," he said. "But I hope I shall see you again some time."

"I hope so, too, Mr. Schoolcraft. And I hope, too, that your interest in my people will continue."

"I know it will."

"Were you at the council, Mr. Schoolcraft?"

"Yes, I was. I heard Sassaba's speech. A misled man, but not, I think, a dangerous one."

"For so many years the Indians have been looking for honest men to guide them that some of them listen to any promise in the wish to find someone among the whites who will keep his word. Sassaba believes the British. But he knows in his heart that Governor Cass is the friend of the Indians. What did you think of the council, Mr. Schoolcraft?"

Henry found it hard to answer immediately. He began to talk thoughtfully. "For one thing, I have now seen enough of the Indians to know that the truth about them doesn't lie in the books I have read, nor yet in the views of voyageurs or many people who live among them," he said. "I want to know much more of them. They seem to me a proud people who live by laws many centuries old. Right now, some of these laws seem to conflict with those of the white men, and that brings trouble."

"Yes, Mr. Schoolcraft, you're right. I'm glad you're seeing them as people. They are proud and sensitive, though they've learned to hide their feelings. They are wise in many simple things, and they are sadly unwise in the ways of other peoples."

"Perhaps some day I can help to interpret them to the white men," said Henry.

"They need someone to do so, Mr. Schoolcraft—someone who does not think of them just as children, or as savages, or as a primitive people to be exploited by those aggressive white men who think only in terms of gold."

Henry himself could not have said any better what lay in his own thoughts. He wanted to sit here beside Jane Johnston for hours, but he knew he must go. So he got up, bade her farewell, and left.

When he looked back, he saw her still standing in the doorway where he had left her. They waved to each other, and for some reason Henry was suddenly elated.

*   *   *

The travelers did not get started until nine o'clock.

Before they could start out, farewells had to be said between the Governor's party and the soldiers under Lt. Pierce, who were returning to Michilimackinac. The Indians who had been with them from Detroit—the Shawnees and the Ottawas—were divided in their wishes, too. Some of them chose to return to their villages above Detroit. Their places were taken by Chippewas from the Sault.

In the afternoon of the second day from the Sault,

they came to the entrance into Lake Superior. They had not yet passed any scene so beautiful. The river led into a deep bay of the lake. It passed out between two jutting points of land, which looked as if, long ago, they had been all one great mountain and had been torn apart just so that the St. Mary could flow out of Lake Superior between the buttes, down to Lake Huron.

Then they were in Lake Superior.

If possible, its water was even more blue than that of Lake Huron, and stretched away as far as they could see. In the north, the Canadian highlands began to fade into the horizon. In the east, along the shore of the lake, a mountain range towered against heaven.

The wind had come up again, so the voyageurs put up the sails. They moved along now as fast as they could have paddled. The steersmen kept their course. Sometimes the shore was very close; sometimes it was far away. The land was rough, with many small bays, yet the beach itself, as much as Henry could see of it, seemed to be sandy or pebbly rather than rocky.

Henry felt that at last they were nearing the heart of the wilderness which was the northwestern portion of the Territory of Michigan. He felt insignificant indeed against the vast blueness of this lake, beside the deep forests and high ridges which marked the shore line. Earth and sky alike were very beautiful and very wild. He thought of himself as an intruder into a domain which

was not his. The air was fresh and fragrant. The strong wind filled the sails, and gave all a feeling of exhilaration.

Yet, even now, after two days, Henry could not forget the events of the council, nor the actions of the Chippewa chiefs. He remembered the unwarranted fear of the women and children, as well as the proud defiance of Sassaba. And he thought often of Jane, who was in part one of them.

Blown by the wind, they passed along the lake without once faltering. The Governor made signs to the other canoes that the party would continue on its way as long as the wind held.

The afternoon faded, the sun went down, and still they went on.

In the twilight they passed the mouth of a river. Three leagues beyond it, in the deeper darkness approaching night, they came to another river just as the wind was beginning to die down.

Now they moved into the river's mouth and pushed for shore.

At once on landing, they saw that they were not alone. Three Chippewa lodges stood back at the edge of the woods. The Indians had seen them coming, and were even now walking in among them, making the traditional signs of friendship with their upraised hands and arms. Some of them carried dried whitefish as a gift to the travelers, seeing which, the Governor ordered that tobacco he brought out to be given them in return.

So the Indians, too, came bearing gifts, thought Henry. Was this not proof that they were not, as Parks had said, always looking for gifts?

There was no chieftain among them, only a *cacique*, who was the son of a chief. The Governor motioned that he should join the circle around the campfire, which was now springing to orange life. One of the party wished to make talk with him.

Parks moved forward and took his place as interpreter.

"What is this river called?" asked Governor Cass.

The Indian, whose name was White Root, answered at great length. Parks translated his reply simply as "Shelldrake River."

Governor Cass looked suspiciously at Parks. "What else did he say?" he pressed Parks. "You aren't giving him his due."

Parks grinned. "He say fishing is good at the mouth of the river. That's w'ere they got the fish they gave us. They have foun' fishing so good they have put up lodges here. He is the son of old Diving Hawk, who has gone to hunt in the southwest. There are many ducks on this river in season. They call the river Shelldrake. That is how he said it."

Governor Cass's eyes twinkled. He did not laugh, because laughter might offend his guest.

"Are there more of you to the west?" asked the Governor.

"Many more. As many as there are stars," answered White Root.

"These fellows like to exaggerate," whispered Doty to Henry. "Where we see one, they see a dozen."

"So do a good many of us," answered Henry with unexpected spirit, so that Doty looked at him in amused surprise.

"Some have gone to fight the Sioux," White Root went on. "If you go far to the west, past the Grand Portage, perhaps you will come to the country of the war."

The Governor pointed at Henry to signify that Henry might like to speak to White Root.

"We are going to the great Father of Waters," said Henry. "Do you know where it is?"

White Root nodded vehemently. "Far west, near the end of the Chippewa country." He said much more, but this was all Parks translated.

"Where does it start?"

White Root was not as talkative at this question. He pondered it for a few moments before he gave an answer. He frowned, shook his head, and said, "Maybe the lake of the Elk."

"Ah, we have La Biche once more," said the Governor dryly. "He doesn't know."

Seeing that White Root could not answer Henry's question about the source of the Mississippi, the Governor made the signs of farewell and said to Parks, "Give him something. A piece of broadcloth and tobacco for the lot of them. Anything. It's high time we got a little sleep."

They were ready to set out not long after seven o'clock next morning.

But they did not get started at that hour. Just as they were about to get into their canoes and push off, one of the Chippewa who was with the party, came back from his lookout to report that someone was coming out of the west. "Big boats," he said. The Indians customarily stood watch, even though there was so little danger at this point that there was no need to do so. But since this was their custom, the Governor did not discourage it.

After listening to the Indian's report, Parks concluded that the boats he described were fur barges. "Most likely from Fond du Lac," he said to the Governor.

"How many are there?"

"Five."

"That could be Morrison. The American Fur Company shipment is due at Michilimackinac. We'll wait. Take a boat out and call him in if he doesn't see us when he goes by."

There was no need to take a canoe out. The voyageurs who paddled the barges saw their camp and turned toward shore. The five barges were heaped high with furs. They came swiftly on toward shore, curling the water back as they pushed onward. At the head of the first barge stood a tall, thick, hard-muscled man of near middle age. He wore a dark moustache and beard. His head, so early in the morning before the sun shone hotly from on high, was uncovered. His long hair flowed back to his shoulders.

This was William Morrison. Henry had heard him spoken of as one of the most ambitious and valuable employees of the American Fur Company. Every year he brought in more furs than any other post in the network which belonged to the Company. As soon as his craft was within jumping distance of shore, he bounded to the land and came striding up to the Governor.

"Governor Cass—and Gentlemen," he said in a booming voice. "I thought this must be your party."

"You were expecting us, Morrison?"

"Looking for you, yes. Sir, word of your coming has gone all up and down the lake. The voyageurs and the Indians alike pass it along. They don't travel as slowly as you. Their cargo is less valuable and—" He paused and grinned.

"And less weighty," the Governor finished for him.

"Now, then, as you see, I'm in haste for Michilimackinac," Morrison went on. "Is there anything I can do for you?"

"We hear rumors of trouble between the Chippewas and the Sioux. What is there to it?"

Morrison shrugged. "There's some fighting, true. But in my opinion the 'war' is just about over."

The Governor called Henry forward and introduced him.

"Sir," said Henry, "can you tell us anything of the headwaters of the Mississippi?"

Morrison looked at him boldly. "I can tell you something of the water between the lake and the Mississippi. But you'll have to find the way yourself." Looking around at the party, he added, "You've enough men, anyway; you can spare a few lost. It's not like traveling a lake."

The Governor grew impatient. "We don't lose men, Morrison."

"But do you know the source, sir?" pressed Schoolcraft.

"Well, there's no doubt but that Leech Lake empties into the Mississippi—so perhaps that's one branch of the source. Then there are several lakes, La Biche . . ."

"La Biche again," groaned the Governor.

"Sir, have you ever heard of a small blue jewel of a lake said to be the true source?"

"That's legend," said Morrison, interrupting him. "I've heard of it many times. But never from one who could lead us there."

Henry was disappointed. It was clear to him that Morrison did not know the source of the Mississippi any more than other travelers who had come from the West. One thing was plain to Henry—he would still have to rely on the Indians of the region where the Mississippi took its origin, in order to find it.

"If you plan to go past the Grand Portage," Morrison went on, "toward the Mississippi, you might find it advisable to think of traveling overland to Sandy Lake from the portages. You're all heavily loaded for the river route."

Henry thanked him and was silent.

The Governor spoke briefly of matters concerning the fur trade. Then, their talk concluded, Morrison bade them all farewell, and returned to his barge. Once more he set off for Michilimackinac. At the same time, the expedition's canoes were pushed off in the opposite direction.

Once again the wind was with them. The sails were put up and the canoes sped along faster than if they had been paddled. They passed swiftly by a party of twenty canoes loaded with Chippewas. The Indians had seen them set out from the river mouth and had turned their canoes in toward those of the expedition. They yelled in their language and made signs that they wished to talk. But the Governor would not stop, despite their signals. Reluctantly he ordered the voyageurs to go on without stopping, for the expedition had already lost too much time.

Parks felt differently. "They only beg for gifts. They are all beggars—an' they are not poor, they only think the white man can be parted easy from such presents."

Henry remembered the Chippewas who had presented the party with food, and he resented Parks' easy dismissal of the Indians. "I don't think you're being fair to them, Parks," he said.

"I know them," answered Parks shortly.

It was on the tip of Henry's tongue to answer hotly that Parks did not know the Indians, that he had only some ideas about them, and that some of these ideas were wrong. But he did not say anything. How could Parks speak of the Indians with the same authority as Jane, whose own mother had been a Chippewa? But little he could say would change Parks' mind.

On they went. Mile after mile of the shoreline was passed and left behind.

The wind, however, could not last. Out of the west, directly toward them, came another storm. The Governor and the voyageurs anxiously watched the cauliflower clouds for some time. Then, at last, when it was apparent that the wind was turning and driving at them from the storm which was now close, the Governor gave the signal to drive to shore.

It was only after they had reached shore, when rain was already beginning to fall, that they saw another canoe on Lake Superior. It was a swift bark canoe, propelled by eight men, but holding in all a dozen voyageurs. It came on with the speed of the wind, directly into the storm. It followed the course of the expedition's canoes and bore in to the same landing place.

"They are after us," guessed Parks.

A few moments later, the Governor identified the canoe as an American Fur Company craft.

Then the voyageurs landed. They had been sent after the Governor by Ramsay Crooks, from Michilimackinac. Dispatches from Detroit had reached the island too late to find the Governor; so Crooks had sent them on.

But this was not all that Crooks had sent.

One among the voyageurs stepped out and introduced himself to the Governor.

"Sir, I am Dufour. I know the place you go to—the country of the Gran' Portage. Mistaire Crooks, he has sent me to sarve you as guide in that country."

The Governor welcomed him heartily wondering what Mr. Crooks would ask of him in return.

Dufour confidently took his place among the party's voyageurs.

The voyageurs of the Company canoe found old friends among those of the expedition, and while the members huddled under the downpour, the voyageurs enjoyed a reunion, quite as if no rain were falling.

But as soon as the rain ended, the Company's men started back for Michilimackinac, and the Governor's party pushed deeper into the wilderness to the West.

Beyond the Pictured Rocks

ON THE FOLLOWING DAY, the nature of the shoreline changed.

First came a towering wall of sand and sandstone. This looked strangely barren after the lush woods they had been passing for so long. Here there were many dead and dying trees, on some of which eagles perched. High overhead wheeled hawks, and black lines of crows filed along the water's edge, in search of food. The change was so great from the scenery which had gone before, that

Henry was amazed. Yet, for a geologist, it was a fascinating change.

Henry noticed, too, that when they were well along this shore, the voyageurs began to scan the sky anxiously.

Henry asked one of the paddlers why he watched the sky so keenly.

"By gar! Bad run ahead," he answered.

"But we're on the lake," protested Henry. He thought of a "bad run" as a region of white water on a river.

The voyageur gave a snort of derision. "You wait, you see. High rocks."

Parks interrupted. "No place to land if the wind come strong, Mr. Schoolcraft. No place at all in the country of picture rocks."

Henry could not imagine what kind of country this could be. Yet the mention of rocks intrigued him, for this was his field. Even as Parks spoke, the great sandbank stretched ahead as far as the eye could see.

But gradually the sandbank grew smaller, and once more forests began to appear. Each time Henry saw a rock jutting out from shore, he thought that they had reached the "bad run" of which the voyageur had spoken. But this did not come for some time, and when it did, Henry was left almost breathless by what he saw.

For now the expedition was passing a region of high bluffs. These bluffs, which were crowned with trees, showed many colors, for most of their sides facing the lake were bare. They showed dark red, white, yellow, brown, green, black—even orange. Caves opened out of them and at the water line, where the pounding waves of Lake Superior had worn away the rock, there were bays.

In one place a great cascade of water arched out from a stream into the lake. It fell almost a hundred feet in a steady, rushing downpour. It was so far out in the lake that the entire expedition could have passed between the falling water and the rock wall without getting a drop of water on anyone. There were other waterfalls, too, and rocky arches reaching into the water.

Henry had never seen anything like it.

He did not once take his eyes from the Pictured Rocks as long as they were opposite the canoe in which he rode. Though the sky was perfectly clear except for one low-lying cloud in the west, the voyageurs were in a hurry to get past the rocks. It was as Parks had said—if a wind-storm rose up suddenly, while they were passing at this place, they would have no haven at which to land. The entire expedition could perish if their canoes were driven against the rocks by the waves which always rose quickly during any storm on Lake Superior.

They passed the Pictured Rocks at last, and soon after reached their goal for the night.

This was the landlocked harbor of Grand Island. The Governor had wanted to reach this place because it was inhabited by a large village of Chippewas from whom the expedition might gather some knowledge of the country to the west. The lodges of the Indians sat well back from the harbor, though in plain sight from the water.

As soon as the Governor's tent was up, the chief of the tribe came to offer the pipe of peace. After he and the Governor had smoked the peace pipe, the Indian spoke through Parks and said that he and his warriors would return in the evening, after the Governor and his party had eaten and rested. But they would do so only if they were welcome.

The Governor assured the chief that they would, indeed, be welcome.

Henry could not help contrasting the great courtesy of these Indians with the often rude boisterousness of members of the expedition—especially the voyageurs, and, even sometimes, the guides.

The Indians did not return until after sundown, but when they came, it was plain to see that they intended to entertain their visitors.

Governor Cass fretted a little about the entertainment. "But at least Henry will like it," he said. "Ever since we've been at the Sault he has become a greater friend of the Indians than any of us."

Henry did not know whether he was serious or making a joke at his expense, because the entertainment was not much different from what he had already seen. It consisted of dances and singing, much in the manner of the Grand Medicine Dance of the Sault.

Alas, it went on, on, on. It kept up until almost everyone in the party wished the Chippewas would forget about entertaining them. But at last the music of gourd rattle, stick-beating, and tambourine did come to an end. The chief announced that several of the tribe wished to make speeches.

"The Chippewa likes to fight, to eat, to hunt, and to talk," said Doty. "He will talk all night if he can."

Governor Cass said that he would listen. He told the Chippewas that he, too, wished to talk with them. He had questions to ask of his red brothers. But he would wait until they had finished.

Thus encouraged, at a gesture from the chief, the first brave came forward to speak. Like all the other Chippewas at this place, he was poorly dressed. Yet he made a fine figure of a man, for he was in good health, and was quite young and handsome.

He addressed the Governor as "Our White Father," and launched into a tale of the bravery of the Indians of his tribe. Henry listened carefully to the translation, for the young Indian spoke with such pride and sincerity, that it was plain to see that for him and his people, his story was an important one. It was such a story as would be told for many generations, handed down from one to another for a long time.

With many gestures, he told how the Chippewas to the north had scolded the Grand Island tribe because they had not made war on the Sioux, as the other Chippewas had done. This had cut deeply into the pride of the Grand Island Chippewas. Even though talk of peace between the nations was even then in progress, thirteen of the Chippewas from the island had gone forth in war-paint. They meant to clear their honor as Chippewas before the entire nation.

He, Spotted Deer, had been one of those chosen. But, alas! he had been named to be the watcher and the teller of the tale. He had not been permitted to fight. Yet he had been among the thirteen who had trekked into the wilderness. They had surprised a large party of Sioux. Because there was talk of peace, the Sioux wished to receive them as friends. They were surprised at the wish of the Chippewas to do battle, especially since they greatly outnumbered the Chippewas. The Chippewas retired for the night, and threw up an earthworks from behind which they would fight. He, Spotted Deer, was posted a distance away.

Then, at dawn, the Chippewas attacked the Sioux settlement. The Sioux were astonished at this brave deed. But the Chippewas were quickly driven back to their earthworks, from behind which they shot at the Sioux. But the Sioux, who greatly outnumbered the Chippewas, surrounded the earthworks and slew them all. Though not before the Chippewas had slain twice their own number.

Then he, Spotted Deer, had undertaken the long and sorrowful journey home. He had come back to Grand Island only a few days before. Now they had shown all the Chippewas that the tribe of Grand Island were not women.

When Parks had finished translating this tale, the Governor had a hard time to keep the displeasure he felt out of his voice. Indians were very sensitive to the tone of a voice; they could tell how the speaker felt by simply listening to the tone of his voice. They did not need to understand his words.

"These Indians and their codes!" he complained. And to Parks, he said, "Ask him whether the warlike spirit of the Sioux has been renewed by the action of the Grand Island Chippewas."

Spotted Deer shook his head. "They consider they have won. They are still ready to talk of truce."

"It is well," said Governor Cass. When Parks had translated this, he added, "Tell him that we stand in awe of the bravery and courage of the Grand Island Chippewa warriors. We ask that they make no further proof of their bravery in this manner, or else there will be none of his red brothers left for the Great White Father to call upon if need be."

This speech pleased all the Chippewas very much.

Henry felt differently from the Governor about the tale of Spotted Deer. Added to what he had already learned about the Indians, Spotted Deer's story told him much about the codes of the Chippewas. They were a fiercely proud people, sensitive to criticism. They held honor above all other virtues. Now he could understand how much it had meant to Sassaba to lose face before his own people in the failure of his defiance of Governor Cass, at the council of the Sault.

The old chief, moved by the Governor's speech, came forward and said, "Our White Father honors us. He honors us in his words. He honors us by his visit. What can we do for our White Father?"

How eager the Chippewas were to please! thought Henry. And how courteous! How little of this aspect of their way of life ever reached the attention of Easterners. And how little of it was seen and taken into account by men like Parks and the voyageurs, who were perhaps goodhearted enough, but rough in their judgments. They tended to think only of the material side of life—of how many furs the Indians might bring in, of how much the Indians could increase the welfare of the trader, and so on.

The Governor pointed to Henry and said, "The Destroyer of Rocks wishes to speak with you."

Henry, amused at the Governor's use of his Indian

name, came quickly forward. "We seek the source of the Great Father of Waters," he said. He wished he could have spoken the language itself, so that it need not be translated by Parks.

The chief's eyelids came down over his eyes. He lowered his head to signify that he was ashamed. He said he did not know where the Great Father of Waters took his beginning. There were many tales of this. A lake known as La Biche. Another, said to be a gem of blue water, ringed round by dense trees. There were yet others. He himself had never been so far to the west. But the Destroyer of Rocks would find there other Chippewas who would be happy to help him in his quest.

He spoke very earnestly and with pained regret.

Henry thanked him gravely.

"We will make medicine to help our White Father," promised the chief.

The Governor now resolved to end the talk with the Indians, even though he knew that other braves would like to speak. He gave the chief presents of broadcloth and passed out several rounds of tobacco. Thereupon the Chippewas retreated to their lodges, shouting in imitation of animals, capering about, and otherwise showing their pleasure.

"These are an interesting but often tiring people, Schoolcraft," said the Governor. "Let us sleep now. We have the Keweenaw Portage ahead of us, and many miles of lake beyond that."

*   *   *

The Keweenaw Portage lay across a long isthmus of land. This isthmus projected forty-five miles out into Lake Superior. In order to reach it, the party would have to cross Keweenaw Bay from Point Abbaye. This was directly across from the mouth of the Portage River, which flowed from within a mile of the opposite side of the isthmus.

From the source of the river, there was a portage of two pauses before they could reach the lake again. A "pause," as Henry understood it from the voyageurs, was the term they used to measure distances. It meant the distance the portaging voyageurs could carry a heavy load before setting it down to rest. They measured every portage by pauses, not by miles. Each pause was about half a mile, but in very rough country it was less than that.

The portage itself represented no risk, explained Parks. When they crossed the bay, they would be in open water. Storms on the lake were sudden and violent, as Henry well knew by this time, and the high waves could easily break a loaded canoe in two.

Though the distance across the bay was only twelve miles, many voyageurs disliked this part of their journey most of all. Indeed, the summer season was the only one in which it could be traveled. In other seasons, the south shore of Lake Superior was so constantly torn by wind and waves that all the voyageurs regularly went around on the Canadian side, even though this was the longer way between the Grand Portage and the Sault.

They did not reach Point Abbaye until afternoon of the second day out from Grand Island. Henry was no longer riding in the Governor's canoe. He was now in Lt. Mackay's canoe with Doty and Captain Douglass.

The sky was overcast, and a light wind blew. The outlook for the journey across the bay was not promising. The voyageurs at the paddles, who were in doubt about crossing, made their objections to Lt. Mackay.

"Let's just follow the Governor's lead," he suggested in answer to them.

They agreed reluctantly, muttering that everyone knew how many chances Governor Cass took. There was the same kind of doubt in the other canoes. Of these, the Indians were the last in the line. They neither spoke nor gestured. But all looked heavenward.

"It doesn't look good," said Doty, watching them. "The Chippewas are more weatherwise than we."

"It's forward," said Lt. Mackay abruptly.

Ahead of them, the Governor's canoe had shot out into the choppy water.

The voyageurs shook their heads, but bent to their

paddles. One by one, the canoes came into line and followed the Governor's lead.

The sky grew darker. The wind came more strongly out of the West. The surface of the lake began to change. The choppy little waves gave place to longer, more rolling waves. When they were an hour away from Point Abbaye, the wind and water were in turmoil. Waves, high enough to engulf them, broke over the canoes, and some of the men made ready to bail.

Yet the Governor's canoe pressed steadily forward.

The voyageurs looked anxiously to Lt. Mackay for a change in their orders. He only motioned them ahead. But at the same time, he broke out more paddles. He handed paddles to Henry, Doty, and Douglass. He himself took one. They knelt among the voyageurs, wherever they could find place, and paddled as vigorously as they could. They were already soaked through by the waves which had drenched them all. Fortunately, the day was warm, and the water was not cold.

Behind them, the other canoes began to turn back. The Chippewas were the first to turn with the wind. Two other canoes followed them. They would now return with the wind at their backs and might reach Point Abbaye safely. Yet they were at that time halfway across, as Lt. Mackay pointed out. There were some among their own voyageurs who wished to turn about, but the Lieutenant would not hear of it.

"If the Governor turns back," he shouted, "we'll do the same. If he doesn't, we won't either."

The Governor did not turn back, so they pushed on. Already soaked, they now had to fear only that the mounting waves might break the frail canoe. As they drove forward, they looked about for any sign that the Governor's canoe had suffered any damage. They found none.

Soon they lost sight of the Governor's canoe all together. One moment it was bobbing about ahead of them; the next it was gone.

They were now too far to turn back. They could only go ahead.

They were grateful that neither rain nor thunder and lightning added to their misery. A torrent of rain might be all that was needed to capsize them. As it was, two men kept the water bailed from the canoe; all of them together could not have kept the canoe free of water if it were raining, and still keep moving the canoe forward.

It seemed hours before Lt. Mackay called out suddenly, "Land ahead!"

Then, in a few minutes, he added, "We're right on course. The mouth of the river lies dead ahead."

Within a short while, they could see their goal—the broad mouth of the Portage River that cut almost across the isthmus. And they saw, too, that a long canoe was drawn well up on the shore. The Governor had reached Keweenaw Point safely.

Soon, they too, were pushing into the quiet of the river's mouth.

At six o'clock the next morning, the other three canoes arrived, having set out before dawn to make up for their defection of the previous day.

Copper Country

IN MID-AFTERNOON of the thirty-fifth day of their journey, they reached the mouth of the Ontonagon River. This was the river that flowed with the color of rust; sometimes it seemed red, sometimes brown. The Governor had told Henry well in advance of their reaching this place that he wished him to examine the region up-river.

He was waiting for Henry when Lt. Mackay's canoe landed.

"Are you tired, Schoolcraft?"

"No more than you, I hope, sir."

"Good. We're leaving at once for the headwaters of the Ontonagon. There's so little time. In a day or two July will be upon us, and we still have a distance to go. We don't know this country, except by word of explorers and traders. Parks has gone to a Chippewa village not far away to find guides, as well as two light canoes more suitable to river navigation. As soon as he returns, we'll set out. The majority of the party will remain here under Major Forsyth's leadership."

Doty pressed forward. "May I go with you, sir?"

"And I?" asked Captain Douglass.

"Very well. We shall take Lt. Mackay and Dr. Wolcott, too."

The tents were being set up well back from the shore. Once before they had made the mistake of camping too close to the water's edge. Then, in the night, huge waves had been whipped up by a storm. The Governor's tent had been washed down, and everything in it had been drenched. Now they made sure that this could not happen again.

Though Parks was not gone an hour, the Governor fretted at his slowness. When he came with two canoes and four Chippewa guides, he seemed well pleased with himself.

"Here they are," Parks said. "They say they know the river."

"I'll talk with them," said the Governor.

Parks motioned the Chippewas to come before the Governor.

They were sturdy Indians. As far as Indian clothing went, they were well dressed. They showed by the way they pointed at the Governor's portly person that they knew he was Big Belly, who spoke for the Great White Father, the friend of the red men and the white men, alike. They were happy to be of service to him. Parks translated questions and answers with great speed.

"You know this river?" asked the Governor, pointing to the Ontonagon.

They nodded eagerly.

"How long is it?"

"More than a hundred miles."

"How far can we go by canoe?"

The four Chippewas consulted among themselves before they made answer. "Not forty miles. Above that, there are many rapids, much white water. We walk to the head of the river from here in four days. From the rapids to the head we go on foot. Hard walking."

The Governor grimaced. This was not welcome news. However able he was in a canoe, Governor Cass found it difficult to carry his weight on foot, for any distance in wilderness country.

The Chippewa spokesman made bold to ask, "What does Big Belly want of the red river?"

The Governor bent and picked up one of the stones

abounding along the river's edge. It had a red-brown color, as did all the shore where the river touched. He pointed to it.

"We wish to find the place where the copper is found."

The Indians broke into smiles. Two of them spoke at once. They knew where the place was. They could lead the Governor straight to it. But it was below the head of the river.

"How far from here?"

"Thirty miles, as the bird flies."

At this, the Governor smiled once more. But he sobered immediately when the Chippewas explained that much of the journey would have to be made over land. Even though the source of the copper was close to the river, it was much farther and more difficult by canoe than it was to leave the river and go over the land to it. The river was very winding and contained many shallow rapids. Nevertheless, the Governor was undaunted.

At six o'clock they began to push up river.

In addition to the Governor, the members of the expedition who had chosen to go, and the four guides, there were in the party enough voyageurs to paddle the canoes. They had loaded only enough supplies for three days.

The Ontonagon here was broad. The river had a winding course and its current was gentle. Its banks were heavily wooded. Dark green branches and vines shadowed the water. Sometimes the trees arched over the river, wide as it was, so that it was as if the two canoes were passing through a green tunnel. Travel on the river was a welcome change from travel on Lake Superior.

It was strange, too, to travel on such oddly colored water after the blue waters they had passed over. Every body of water Henry had seen from Detroit northwest had been as blue as the sky. The water of the Ontonagon was tinted by the copper and iron deposits of that river's valley.

After an hour's journey, the guides made signals to the voyageurs to slow down and bear to the right.

"What is it now?" bawled the Governor.

Parks repeated his question and listened to what the nearest of the guides replied. "It ain't much," he said. "The Chippewa keep a sturgeon fishery up here. The opening for fish and canoe is to the right."

Parks had hardly finished speaking, when they swept around a bend in the river and came upon the fishery. It lay across the river in the form of a simple dam.

"They make a living this way," said the Governor to Henry.

The bottom of the river was less than four feet deep at this point. Henry paid particular attention to the way the fishery was made. The Chippewas had driven enough sharpened saplings into the bottom of the river to reach almost from one shore to the other. These were supported by crotched stakes braced against the current. The saplings were inclined downstream, and against the sides of these inclined stakes, the Indians had placed long poles. They had secured the poles by hickory withes in such a way that the fishermen could not only pass from one end to the other of the dam, but could also sit and fish at any place.

They fished with iron hooks, which were fixed to the ends of long slender poles. There were five Indians busily fishing as the canoes came up. As Henry watched, two of them brought up large sturgeons. The hooks, however, were not baited. They were just lowered into the water, and whenever an Indian felt a fish pressing against the pole, he would jerk up his hook suddenly, and with such skill, that he would almost always bring up a sturgeon with it. Of course, there were many sturgeon moving in the waters of the Ontonagon for they were coming down stream at this season, having been up the river to spawn.

Governor Cass signaled to the voyageurs to stop for a little while so that all of them might watch the sport. The fish that were brought up by the hooks were quite large. Some were as large as four feet in length, though most of them were between two and three feet long. Through Parks, the Chippewas explained that the Indians of the Ontonagon relied almost entirely on this sturgeon fishery

for a living. They cut the fish into thin slices and dried or smoked it. The fishery was more than fifty years old.

Before they left, one of the fishermen came over to them and gave the Governor his largest catch. Henry looked toward Parks to see whether there was any recognition on the interpreter's part that here, once again, was evidence that the Indians were not just "beggars," as he had described them. The fisherman asked for nothing; he might not even have known the Governor, though Henry supposed that he did. He had simply come over and offered his prize catch to the man who had given the order to stop. Nor did he wait to receive a gift in return, but walked away at once and resumed his fishing.

Apparently Parks did not see anything inconsistent with his attitude and the acknowledgment that these Chippewas made a living by means of this fishery. These Indians were not beggars. Just because there were a few Indians—just as there were white men—who begged, Parks had no right to indict an entire nation for the faults of a few. Henry remembered again how proud Jane Johnston had sounded when she had spoken of her Indian mother, and he understood how right she was to feel proud.

Soon they were beyond the sturgeon fishery. Now the late twilight of the region was beginning to fall, for here in the heart of the woods, darkness came more swiftly than it did on the lake. And it did not come half so gloriously, for the heavens which were filled with the peach and copper afterglow over the lake, were here almost concealed behind the trees.

"Look for a place to camp," instructed the Governor at last.

The Chippewa guides motioned ahead. There was a place scarcely half an hour away, they said. It was a great bar of sand in the middle of the river. If the Governor had no objection, they could make camp on this sandy island.

Despite a horde of mosquitoes, they made camp there, and prepared for a difficult night. It was not yet dark when the sandbar came into sight.

At four o'clock in the morning, they were on the way again. The shores of the river were still heavily wooded with dense forests where no ax had ever rung. Maple, elm, and walnut trees crowded down to the water's edge. With them grew thick underbrush, and great masses of vines which crowned trees and trailed down into the water.

But as they moved up the river, the character of the land changed. The low country which had maintained since they had left the river's mouth, gave way to more and more hills, which reached higher and higher the farther they went. At the same time, the Ontonagon was getting narrower and white water began to appear. At first these rapids were not difficult to pass through, but soon rocks began to add to their difficulties.

Suddenly, only three hours after they had started, the Chippewa guides called a halt.

"Canoes too full," said their spokesman. "We walk now."

"How far?" asked the Governor.

"Twenty miles."

"Twenty miles would kill me," said the Governor. "Is there no other way?"

The Chippewa explained that if the canoes were lightened by half, they could go farther up the river. That meant that some of them would have to walk from here. Yet all could meet at a path the Chippewas had made beside the river, a path that led to the place where the copper came from.

Henry immediately volunteered to walk. So did Doty, Captain Douglass, Lt. Mackay, and some of the voyageurs. Two Indian guides leaped from the canoes to accompany the overland party.

None of them, except the Chippewas, had any idea of how rugged the walk would be. The guides struck into the woods at once. They seemed to have a sense of direction which led them straight to any point they wished to go to, for they went off in diagonal fashion from the river and did not swerve except for an occasional fallen tree.

Unhappily, the Indians gave no thought to the difficulties of the way they had chosen. They led the party through deep woods, over ridges, down ravines, through desolate regions of shattered rocks, and across chasms, on fallen logs. The guides walked very swiftly.

It was soon plain that only the guides were used to traveling so rapidly on foot over such rough terrain. Henry, Doty, Douglass, Lt. Mackay—all were soon so tired that they wanted to drop wherever they were, regardless of the mosquitoes and deerflies which tormented them. Soon the voyageurs began to tire, too.

But the guides never halted. On and on they went. Henry began to wish he had not been so hasty about volunteering to walk. Yet he knew he would do so again, to save the Governor, for the older man could never have made such a trip as this.

They did not pause for five hours.

Then, when they had walked fifteen miles, the guides suddenly stopped. Henry saw that they had reached a kind of path. It was not far from the Ontonagon, perhaps two or three miles. The character of the vegetation told as much, since it was the same as that through which they had passed immediately after leaving the canoes.

Here they sat down to wait. The guides made signs to say that it was to this place that the others from the canoes would come.

The reason for the guides' haste was soon clear—the journey by water was shorter. They had not been waiting very long when the rest of the party came in from the direction of the river.

The Governor, walking unsteadily, followed the guides and sat down heavily.

"I can't take this, Gentlemen," he announced at once. "You'll have to go on without me. I've been clambering up hills and down until I feel I can't walk another step. It's six miles more from here. I'll have all I can do to get back to the Ontonagon."

There was an immediate parley. It seemed a shame that, having come so far, the Governor could not go on. Perhaps if they rested longer?

"No," said the Governor, shaking his head. "That would mean the loss of more time. We can't afford it."

Governor Cass would not change his mind. In truth, Henry thought, he did look worn out. His face was very red and his clothing was wet with perspiration. In addition, he had been bitten many times by mosquitoes, the deerflies had raised great lumps on his skin, and both hands and face had been scratched by briars and branches. He was weak from so much walking, to which he was completely unaccustomed. In his youth, he had walked as much as any of them, but he was now too heavy and too old for hard walking.

"You go on," he said. "I must rest. Henry, you can report on what you find there. We're anxious to know whether there are extensive copper deposits. Then there's a story of a great mass of pure copper along the river. Let us learn how much this has been exaggerated."

"Depend on me, sir."

"I do, Henry. Now, as for me, I intend to return to the river at the place where we've left the canoes—once I've got my breath back. Let us meet there, when the mission to the mines has been accomplished. Then we'll get back in haste to the mouth of the river."

Knowing that they could not change the Governor's mind, the rest of the party started out again for the region of the copper mines.

The Governor Is Missing

THE WAY BEFORE THEM was the same as it had been for the previous five hours, one of deep forests, desolate rocky areas, hill country. Once again the Chippewa guides forged ahead at a rapid pace. The white men did not wish to lag behind, for white men among Indians always tried to do as well or better in anything the Indians did, since Indians respected any skill greater than their own, and scorned any that was less.

At last, in less than two hours, they reached a region of copper deposits.

The guides took Henry directly to the copper mass of which the Governor had spoken. It was not as large as he had expected it to be. It lay on the edge of the river, at the foot of a high clay bluff, just opposite an island. It looked as if it had slipped down off the face of the bluff. At one time, surely, it had been part of the bluff. One earlier explorer, who had seen it, said that it was about five tons, but Henry was confident it was not much over a ton. Even so, this was a very large mass of pure copper. It was one of the largest in the world. Indeed, Henry knew of only one piece that was larger, and that had been found in Brazil.

When he looked around him, Henry saw that the copper region was too extensive to examine as thoroughly as he would have liked. He could spend days traveling through it. This place was perhaps only one of many others which showed copper. The Chippewas called it their copper "mines" only because they were able to pick up pieces of pure copper in this vicinity. The great mass of copper could be worked and cut, if the Governor wished to undertake it. What could be done with the other copper in the vicinity remained to be seen.

He took out his little hammers and broke several stones of various kinds which he found here and there. In each of them he found traces of copper. Of course, he had chosen the stones he had broken especially because he thought he would find such traces.

The other members of the party watched him with interest. Now and then they teased him a little, for he had to work while they rested.

The Indians, however, crowded around him wherever he went. Each time he picked up a stone, the Indians hurried to pick up others like it and offer them to him. This was just what the Shawnees and Ottawas had done earlier in the trip. Henry always accepted their stones and broke them apart, which delighted them. How curious they were! How eager to learn!

He spent over an hour studying the region and the outcropping of rock on it. He collected as many specimens as he could carry without putting too much more of a burden on himself for the return trip. Then he said that he was ready to return.

The others, who had rested, at once started up. They began the long trail back to the meeting place with the Governor.

When they reached the place of the canoes, no one was there.

They were astounded. The Governor and his guides had started back hours before. What had happened to them? Alarm for the Governor's safety fell like a pall upon the party.

Doty and Douglass were all for returning along the trail without delay. But the hour was now late. Besides, if the Governor and his guides had been anywhere near the trail, they would have heard the party passing. The voyageurs who had chosen to remain with the canoes had not seen or heard of the Governor since he had set out to meet the overland travelers. They had concluded that he was with them and had not been looking for him. Consequently, they were now as surprised and upset as the members of the party back from the copper mines.

All tried to imagine what might have happened to Governor Cass. He might have fallen into one of the chasms from the dangerous log crossings. Fearing that they would be blamed, his Chippewa guides might have run away to hide. He could also have injured himself and been unable to walk. The guides could not have carried him. Just the same, one of them could have come to let the rest of them know. Bears or wolves might have beset him and the guides.

And what would become of the expedition if anything happened to the Governor? For himself, Henry vowed that he would go on.

"Suppose it's nothing as serious as we imagine," said Henry suddenly.

"Then why aren't they here?" demanded Captain Douglass.

"Wouldn't they have tried to reach the river, no matter what happened?" asked Henry. "I think they would. Let's send a canoe up the river as far as we can go."

"It's all but dark!" protested Doty.

"Then it will be just as dark where the Governor is."
He looked around him. "Who'll go with me?"

Guides and voyageurs immediately responded. The other members of the expedition preferred to remain and wait, on the chance that the Governor might still come into camp.

Keeping the canoe as light as possible, Henry and his companions began to move up the river in the twilight. They traveled swiftly into the growing darkness. All manner of strange sounds now came out of the forest, which was a wilderness in which lived lynx and wolves, fox, deer, and bear, as well as many kinds of birds whose strange cries continued to come from the woods even after darkness had enfolded the trees.

Henry hoped, despite his fears.

There were, after all, three men beside the Governor. All were armed. It was hard to believe that any one animal or group of animals could have overcome them. There were not believed to be any hostile Indians in this country. But there was always a remote chance that a war party of Sioux could have come through the wilderness bent on warring upon Chippewas, just as the Chippewas of Grand Island had traveled into the West to war on Sioux. Such a party might have attacked and slain the Governor and his guides.

They did not begin to fire their weapons to attract attention until they were some distance from the camp they had left. Even then, answering shots could be heard from below. But there was also a sound from far ahead.

Henry did not dare to believe that it was a shot, lest he be disappointed. "What do you think?" he asked the voyageurs.

"That *was* shot!" said one excitedly. "I know!"

"Shoot again," said another.

Henry and the voyageurs fired another round. The echo sounded and resounded on the river.

This time, unmistakably, shots came from up ahead.

Though they moved as fast as they could up the river in the direction of the shots, they had to make frequent stops for rapids. Since it was now dark, they did not dare to run them. They had to move into shore, lift out the canoe, and portage it through the woods. Luckily, the moon lent its feeble light and helped them to find their way. Each time they were grateful to reach the water again, only to be sent to shore by more rapids.

Then, suddenly, coming around a bend, they saw the glow of a campfire. They turned toward it at once.

There sat the Governor and his guides, all unharmed.

Henry shouted with joy and relief.

As the canoe touched shore, he jumped out and embraced the Governor, who had struggled to his feet.

"What happened, sir? We had almost given you up."

"Why, we got lost," answered the Governor. He was fairly bristling with indignation. "These guides of ours fell to arguing which way to go. One wanted to go that way, one this. We went the middle way. In no time at all no one knew where we were. I tell you, we were lucky to come out on the river at all. By the time we did, I was just too tired to move a step farther."

"Well, the canoe will hold us all. You'll have to walk around a few places of white water down river a little way, but you'll manage that," said Henry.

He helped the Governor into the canoe and took his place behind him. The guides, none saying a word and all heartily ashamed of themselves, got in, too. They set out down river.

In less than an hour they were reunited with the other members of the party, who greeted them with fervent cheers.

*   *   *

Ten miles down river next morning, Henry was delighted by another insight into the way the Chippewas lived. The guides motioned the canoes toward the east bank of the river. They explained through Parks that they wanted to examine a bear trap they had set there some time ago. The Governor nodded his consent, and the canoes put in to shore.

Sure enough, a bear had been caught. The trap was made of logs, set up in such a way that when the bear crept underneath to seize the bait which was left there, the logs would fall on him. There he was, his hind legs held down by the heavy logs. His fore paws, which were free, had savagely torn everything within his reach.

The entire party left the canoes to look at the bear. It was a very large beast and growled furiously at them. If it could have freed itself, it would have attacked them without a moment's hesitation. Its great body was five feet long, and weighed more than three hundred pounds. It was now necessary to shoot the bear, so that the Chippewas could claim the carcass.

But the Indians themselves appeared to be very reluctant to shoot it. They persuaded Lt. Mackay to do so. The Lieutenant leveled his gun and shot the bear twice. The bear slumped slowly to the ground and lay still.

One of the voyageurs, knowing of Henry's interest in the Indians, plucked at his sleeve and whispered, "Now watch this."

One of the Chippewa guides was already walking up to the bear. He wore a broad smile on his face. Coming up to the bear, he made a low bow and spoke to it. He said to it, "Hai, Muckwah!" Then he bent, took hold of the bear's nearest paw, and shook it. He spoke to the dead bear at some length in the Chippewa language. In the course of his address, he pointed to Lt. Mackay, calling him "Chemoquemon."

"What is he saying?" asked Henry.

The voyageur grinned. "He ask the bear, Muckwah,

to forgive heem that he has kill' heem, but it was the American—Chemoquemon—who fire' the shots. These Indians, they hol' the bear in great esteem. They do not kill many. But when they do, they use every part of the bear. They like the flesh to eat. They wear the skin. They make the claws into a piece for the neck. They use the oil for themselves and to sell; they rub it on the skin to protec' them from the mosquitoes. But the bear is a pairson to the Indians. He, too, is the child of the forest, the child of Manitou, just as they are. So they ask the bear's pardon for kill' him. That is to make sure he will not give bad talk against them to the Great Manitou."

What a strange custom! thought Henry. And yet, was it not also simple and beautiful? It was an expression of the Indian's awareness that all things which had life had a right to enjoy that life. It was proof of the Indians' belief that the Great Manitou watched over all His creatures, great and small. This was part of a religion in which the Indians had faith. Surely, thought Henry, it was not so very different from the religion of the white man!

Now that the bear had been spoken to, the Chippewas were hurrying about to extricate the bear from the fallen logs, and to re-set the trap. They did not wish to delay the Governor and his party, knowing how sensitive to the waste of time the Governor was.

As soon as the bear was loaded into one of the canoes,

they set out once more for the mouth of the Ontonagon.

*   *   *

In the evening before they left the camp at the mouth of the river for the long journey to the Fond du Lac, the expedition was entertained by Chippewas from the nearby village. All the Indians of the tribe came over with a specially chosen party who were to dance for the Governor.

For the most part the Chippewa dancers wore only leggings and breech clouts, with kneebands and belts of wampum work. One or two of them wore the shirts the Governor had given them. Some did not wear leggings at all. But all of them were painted, even to the legs. One Indian had his legs painted black. There were circles of red and black around the middle of his thighs, and his face was covered with yellow, red and black paint. Some of them were painted all in black; some in black and red. All had transverse stripes of red around their foreheads, temples, and cheeks.

The dances did not begin until one of the young chiefs came in with his own flag. He put it down opposite the Governor's tent. As soon as he had done so, the music began. The music was the same he had heard before, and, indeed, the dance which was then begun and was called the Pipe Dance, was also the same.

Most of the members of the expedition were very

tired of the Indian dances. Henry alone watched with absorbed interest. He was keenly aware that every movement the Indians made in the dance had a special meaning, and he wished very much that he could understand everything they said and did. How much easier it would be, he thought, if only he could speak to them in their own language and ask them to tell him the meaning of their dances and customs.

Perhaps some day he might learn their language. Once again he thought of Jane Johnston. How easy and pleasant it would be if she could be persuaded to teach him the Chippewa language! She spoke it like the Indians. The more he thought of it, the more he was convinced that Jane might do it. She was convinced of his sincere interest in the Indians, and she would know as well as he— perhaps better—how necessary it was for him to understand and speak the language of the Indians before he could hope to interpret them to his fellowmen. For this, he was now convinced, he must do, lest the Indians be forever misunderstood.

As he watched the conclusion of the Pipe Dance and the beginning of the Buffalo Dance, Henry could see plainly by the joyous expressions on the faces of the Indians, how much they enjoyed dancing. They were happy, and they were proud of their ability thus to entertain their visitors. The Buffalo Dance was quite easy for Henry to understand, except for a few movements.

It was a riotous dance, in which a large number of the Chippewas took part. They danced in a circle around the young chief's flag, where the glow of the campfire made weird shadows dance on their shiny bodies. They whooped and yelled. They stared fiercely to right and left. Once in a while one of the dancers threw himself down on all fours and rubbed his head against the flagstaff. Others rubbed heads together. Still others tried to roll. All this was supposed to imitate the buffalo. Even the children joined in this dance, taking the part of the buffalo calves, and the entire ring of dancers soon grew to look like a herd of the animals they were imitating.

Much to Henry's regret—but at the same time greatly to the relief of everyone else—the Governor stopped the dances. He could not have done this directly, without deeply offending his guests. But he could do so indirectly. As soon as the Buffalo Dance was finished, he signaled to Parks to bring forward gifts for the dancers. And when Parks came with the gifts, the Governor simply retired to his tent.

The moment the Governor disappeared, the Chippewas stopped their dances. They knew what was coming, and they watched Parks with eagerness, yet with great dignity. And as soon as they had received their gifts, they ran off in the direction of their village, whooping and yelling.

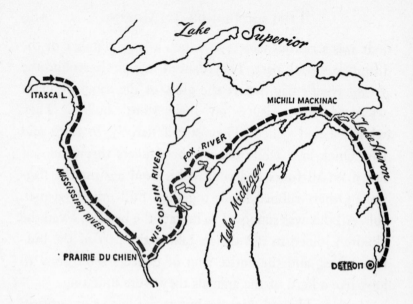

The Fond du Lac

AT NOON of the forty-third day of their journey, they saw the last of Lake Superior. They now entered the region of the Fond du Lac, the country at the foot of the lake. Their canoes swung into the St. Louis River, which would lead them in the direction of the Mississippi.

Though the river was narrow at its mouth, it soon widened into a broad stream a mile across. It looked more like a small lake than a river. It abounded in birds and wild rice. The Chippewas, he said, harvested this rice in September. They passed among it in canoes at harvest time and beat the rice down into blankets which were spread over the bottom of each canoe to catch it. This was an important food of the Chippewas and the Winnebagos.

Far ahead of them rose a range of high ridges. This range, which cut across the northern sky, was the barrier they would have to cross before they could hope to reach the Mississippi. The St. Louis River had worn its way through the mountains, but the river was too rough and rugged in many places to travel by boat. There were many portages on the St. Louis River, one of which consisted of nineteen pauses and was at least eight miles in length.

It was a region that had been inhabited for many decades.

They passed a Chippewa village of fourteen lodges not far from the river's mouth. Quite near by, above this village, on the opposite shore, rose the ruins of one of the old Northwest Fur Company forts and trading houses, which had been abandoned six years before. Instead of rebuilding it, the American Fur Company had chosen the site of the first portage for their new fort.

They reached this fort at seven o'clock that evening. The Fond du Lac department headquarters could not really be called a fort, as Henry saw at once. It consisted of several low log buildings, which made up three sides of a square. The open side was toward the river. These buildings contained a warehouse, a canoe-yard, a house for the resident clerk, and places for voyageurs to sleep. There were four acres of garden and some animals. Henry counted three horses, two oxen, three cows, and four bulls.

The resident clerk of the fur company came from his house to meet them. He was a tanned young man with a heavy moustache. He was muscular and stocky, but not heavy. His name was Pierre Cotte. He and his brother Joseph were in charge during the absence of William Morrison, who had not yet returned from Michilimackinac. He came down to the shore and saluted the Governor.

"Greetings, Governor!" he called out. "You'll be happy to know that we've ordered a supper spread for you and your party."

"We'll do justice to it, Cotte," the Governor assured him.

The Governor stepped out of the canoe and clasped Cotte's hand. Cotte was an old friend. Governor Cass knew just about every white man in the Territory of Michigan, as well as most of the Indian chiefs.

"Come, sir, you'll be hungry and tired."

"When have I not been since I began this journey!" cried the Governor.

At supper, the clerk asked about the journey. How had it gone? And now where did they intend to go?

"To the Mississippi," answered the Governor. "There,

Mr. Schoolcraft expects to locate the source of that river. Afterward, we hope to pass down it to Prairie du Chien. Thence up the Wisconsin, down the Fox, up Lake Michigan to Michilimackinac, and back down Huron to Detroit."

"It will be October before you're home again."

"Perhaps it will. We shall see."

"But how are you going from here?"

The Governor told him, recalling what Morrison had said during their brief visit that morning on Lake Superior.

Cotte's open face looked troubled. "But you know, sir, you can't hope to carry these large canoes far up the river. When you come to the Great Detour the men will be unable to carry them."

"I had thought as much," said the Governor agreeably.

"Perhaps you would permit me to arrange an exchange at the foot of the Grand Portage, sir. That will permit you to send back the two large canoes you have and take four smaller craft instead. These are much more suited to inland waters. They'll carry you at least to Green Bay— or all the way back to Detroit, if you wish."

"Agreed," replied the Governor without hesitation.

"If there's anything further we can do for you, sir, please name it."

"We'll need some of the local Indians on hire to see us over the portages."

"I'll see to it, sir. They'll be ready in the morning."

Cotte was as good as his word. In the morning no less than thirty Chippewas were at hand. There were not only the men, but also their wives. It was understood that the women would carry as much as the braves.

*   *   *

The Great Detour was reached in four miles.

This was the portage that led into the heights and across. By the time the last of the canoes came in, the first of them was already being unloaded. Some of the goods were being taken along the first pause. The voyageurs were in the habit of taking all the supplies and provisions to the first stopping place, no matter how many trips back and forth it took to do this. Then to the second, and so on.

The Governor protested this method. "Why not carry it all the way to the other side, while you have it on your shoulders?" he asked.

"We do not do it thees way," answered a spokesman for the voyageurs.

"I suggest you try it," said the Governor.

"No, sair, forgeeve us. We do not. You see, sair, the men, they are very tired when they carry. They take goods to the pause; then they come back. It is relief to them to be able to walk thees way back free of goods. They then are fresh for another load."

This explanation made good sense to Governor Cass. Good-naturedly, he waved the voyageurs on.

The supplies, which had been added to at the Fond du Lac department, were meant to serve them until they reached one of the posts on the Mississippi, below the place where they would first enter upon that river, which was at Sandy Lake. As a result, they were loaded to their utmost capacity. Neither the voyageurs nor the Indians could be expected to save many hours in the carrying if everyone did not help. But the members of the party had not suspected that they, too, must take a hand until the Governor announced, "We will all carry, Gentlemen."

Each of the members of the expedition began by taking his own belongings first. They took a hand with good grace, since all knew that unless they did so they would be on the portage many more days than they planned. As it was, it would take several days to cross the Great Detour.

The trail was very rough. It went almost straight up from the foot of the portage. In addition to the roughness of the trail, the temperature soared. It grew sultrier as the day advanced, and very hot. Muttering clouds along the horizon promised rain, but in the meantime the sun beat down without even a fleece of cloud to cover it to give them some relief.

The country through which they passed was wild and rugged. Sometimes they walked among rocks. Then they went through swamps, sinking deep into mud. Sometimes they had to clamber over fallen trees. All around them the dark forest of hemlocks and pines whispered as in a wind, and from a distance came the steady roaring of the rushing waters of the river, cascading down toward the lower land and on to Lake Superior.

Henry carried a hundred pounds on his shoulders. By the time he had covered half the first pause, he thought he would not make it to the resting place. But each time he felt too tired, he looked toward one of the Indians who had been hired by Cotte to help.

This Indian was so elegant in his stature that Captain Douglass had immediately named him Lord Byron. No one knew any other name for him. He was as strong as an ox. At one time he carried two kegs of bacon, which weighed over a hundred pounds each, a bag of flour or corn about a hundred pounds in weight, and some other pieces. With such a heavy load, he went so fast that he could not be said to be walking. Rather, he seemed to trot.

Lord Byron's example was almost equaled by that of the Indian woman who was his mother. She carried at one load, a birch canoe large enough to bear a whole Indian family with all their possessions; at another, she carried mats and birch bark for a wigwam, three Indian bags of skins, fishing tackle, and a large camp kettle with all the cooking apparatus and eating utensils of the camp.

Most of the men carried loads only slightly less than Lord Byron's. Among them was Dufour, who was now in first position as guide, since this was his country, and he knew it better than any of the guides who had come from Detroit or the Sault.

But there was one thing Dufour did not know, as Henry had taken the trouble to find out. He did not know where the Mississippi took its rise, though he was familiar with all the legends Henry had already heard.

The baggage was carried to the first pause and piled up there. Then the carriers returned to the beginning of the portage for another load. Thus there was always a double line of carriers—some going up, and some coming down empty-handed. The voyageurs made good-natured fun of the members of the expedition. The "gentlemen," they said, were weak men. Some of them sang voyageurs' songs in French and French-Canadian dialect as they climbed along the rough trail. The Chippewas, on the other hand, worked without making a sound.

Henry had often heard accounts of how lazy the Indians were. Just as often he had seen evidence to the contrary, most recently at the fishery of the Ontonagon River. But here the Indians worked so hard that no one outdid them, not even the practised voyageurs. Nor did they show the effects of this hard work, which made

Henry believe that they were accustomed to it. Otherwise, they would certainly have appeared tired as a result of doing such unaccustomed labor.

On what was left of the first day of the portage, they covered five pauses. Then they camped. Their exhaustion, however, was not to know much rest. Their camp did not include wigwams or any other cover. They lay under the open sky, and, during the night, rain began to fall. By morning, they were wet through. Had it not been for the heat, they might have been in danger of taking cold or, worse still, pneumonia.

Though the downpour of rain continued through the dawn, the carriers were up at sunrise. Rain was not enough to delay them, even though the rain made the portage twice as difficult. Mud and water squelched under foot wherever they walked, except in the rocky places.

There were more swamps to cross, many rocky precipices to skirt, and dark and gloomy forests to pass through. Henry thought more than once that it would have been bad enough to walk without being burdened with baggage. The heavy burdens he and the others carried made the journey much more difficult.

Only the voyageurs kept up their spirits. They sang and joked from one pause to another. They drove themselves all the harder during the bad weather. They picked up large loads of supplies and put them down again at the next pause. They went back for another load and

then another. Henry had had no real idea of how much weight they were carrying until he had to help carry it. It was so, too, of the other members of the expedition. Portaging was part of the voyageur's life; it was not part of the lives of the men who traveled in Governor Cass's party.

On the third day, they came to the end of the Great Detour.

Here the St. Louis River flowed along at a greater height than at the beginning of the portage. They were now almost three hundred feet higher. The mountains were far higher than this, but the river had cut its way down through them many hundreds of years ago.

They now had seven smaller canoes, more suited to river travel. Pierre Cotte had sent the four canoes he had promised. They had been waiting at the beginning of the portage, and had been among the first objects to be brought to the end of the portage for they had had to be repaired before they could be loaded again. Many holes and tears had been made in them during the portage.

The party got under way just as soon as the loading had been completed.

They had gone only six miles when they came to another portage. This one, said Dufour, was known as the Portage of Knives. Its name had been given because of the great amount of slate which lay in a vertical position, cutting and bruising the feet of travelers, especially those of the moccasined Indians. At sight of this portage so close to the Great Detour, the Governor remembered the advice Morrison had given him and called a council.

"Gentlemen," he said, "we're faced with ever more and more portages. Mr. Dufour tells me it's possible to reach Sandy Lake by land, which agrees with the information Mr. Morrison gave us. It's plain that I'm not built to walk very far or for very long. You saw that at the Ontonagon. It may be that some of you would like to try the overland route. Once we're at Sandy Lake, we're virtually at the Mississippi, since the lake opens to that river."

"How far is the overland trail?" asked Doty.

"Two days' journey, if all goes well," said Dufour. "But it could be twice that, if you were to meet trouble."

"I'll send along eight soldiers under Lt. Mackay," said the Governor, "and we'll meet at the Sandy Lake post. There are two Chippewa guides available—I trust they'll perform more effectively than those of the Ontonagon. I hesitate to pick and choose among you, and prefer to leave the matter to your own choice. Will any of you gentlemen chance it?"

"I, for one," said Henry.

Doty's voice came almost at the same moment.

There was but a brief hesitation before Trowbridge and Chase likewise decided to go overland.

The Governor looked long and hard at Henry. "I don't

want you to feel you ought to go, Schoolcraft. After all, the others will rest at Sandy Lake until we go down river. You'll be going up the river—no one knows for how long —before you go back down. They'll be resting a long time, and you will rest hardly at all."

"Thank you, but I prefer the overland trip."

"Very well."

There were sixteen in all, since the Governor appointed Parks to go along. As Dufour could speak the Chippewa language, Parks was not needed by the Governor. An interpreter would be needed by the overland party, for there were Chippewas at Sandy Lake, and it would be necessary to have someone who knew their language when they met. It was important that Parks be one of the overland party.

Overland to Sandy Lake

THEY LEFT THE CAMP at the head of the portage at six o'clock next morning. Each of the men carried not only a pack with provisions for five days, but a knife, a cloak or blanket, and some protection against mosquitoes, as well. Not all of them carried arms. Guns would only add weight to each traveler's load, and they needed to do away with all unnecessary weight. Only the soldiers carried arms. The country was said to be friendly, but the men might want to hunt game on the way.

The trail was at first plainly marked. It led through a closely grown forest of pine and hemlock, winding and twisting about among the trees. Two miles from the portage, they came to an Indian path which led in the same direction they were going. So they followed this.

Suddenly both path and trail came to an end. They had come to a swamp, which stretched ahead of them for several miles. But the guides did not hesitate to cross it, and the men followed closely.

Thereafter the country changed abruptly. From swamp to dry sandy barrens, covered with shrubbery and scrub pines. Then to another forest of hemlock and spruce, and on to a small lake. Since they had no canoes, they were forced to go around it. They walked through thick woods and mucky swamps, climbing over fallen trees, struggling through clinging mud, until at last, in desperation, they decided to follow along the shore of the lake, sometimes even walking in the water.

It occurred to Henry presently that the Chippewa guides did not seem too certain of their way. They consulted together frequently in low voices, and looked this way and that in some perplexity.

Parks agreed with Henry. He had no very high opinion of them as guides, and said frankly that the Chippewas were lost. Nevertheless, they followed the guides when at last they struck out through a tamarack swamp.

The day had been one of mixed sunshine and rain. It was now five o'clock. They had walked eleven hours and had traveled close to twenty miles, and now they were ready to encamp for the night. The guides were only too pleased to stop, for they were unsure of their course.

Before setting out in the morning, the Chippewa guides left a message for other Indians who might travel this way. With their knives, they put a number of figures and signs upon a large piece of birch bark. All Chippewas would understand this picture language. The sheet of bark was then stuck into the end of a blazed pole which was driven into the ground in such a way that it leaned in the direction in which they were traveling.

Henry studied it intently. First, the Indians had drawn figures for the entire party. The Indians were pictured without hats; the white men with hats. Lt. Mackay was shown with a sword, which signified that he was an officer. Eight muskets stood for the eight soldiers. Doty was shown with a book, because, Parks explained, the Chippewas thought he was a lawyer. Henry was shown with the hammer he always carried in his belt. The Indians had also drawn figures of a tortoise and a prairie chicken, which they had killed. Three pictures of rising smoke signified three camp fires. Parks was shown as a white man with a tongue outside his mouth. This meant that he

was the interpreter. Finally, three hacks on the pole signified that the journey would take three days, and not
the two Dufour expected.

Any Chippewa reading this sign would know that a
party of white men, guided by two Indians and guarded
by eight soldiers under an officer, were on their way to
Sandy Lake.

The guides, who had all along disagreed with Dufour's
guess about the length of the overland journey, were more
right than Dufour. It was noon of the fourth day after
they had quitted the main body of the expedition at the
Portage of the Knives when they saw the post at Sandy
Lake.

Unfortunately, they found themselves on the far side
of the post, across the lake. They had mounted the last
pine ridge, and there, on the other side, almost directly
opposite them, stood the buildings of the American Fur
Company post. Sandy Lake, in which were many islands,
was five miles long and four miles wide.

Henry gazed with dismay at the position of the post.
Would they have to walk all the way around one end of
the lake? They were so very tired. The fort seemed so
near and yet was so far away!

Henry remembered that Pierre Cotte had told him that
a gun shot at any place around the lake could be heard all
the way to the fort. The clerks would hear the shot and
be sure to investigate. Henry carried a letter for them;

it had been given to the Governor by Cotte, who in turn, had given the letter to Henry to present to the two clerks, Ashman and Fairbanks.

"Let the soldiers fire their weapons," he suggested. "They may hear us and send canoes across."

Lt. Mackay gave the signal to fire.

They waited expectantly for someone to appear on the lake, but there was no response. After a short time, the soldiers fired a second round, and again they waited.

Still nothing.

A third round was fired, and still no sign of life.

Just when they had given up and were preparing to leave for the long trek around the lake, Parks shouted and pointed to a boat coming cautiously across the lake. They could not see whether it was manned by Indians or white men.

"Let them see the soldiers," said Henry.

They all marched down to the lake's edge, the soldiers in front. Some of them shouted; one or two fired their weapons. Finally, an answering shot from the canoe told them they had been seen.

At last the canoe came close enough so that they could see two white men in it. But where were the Indians? There were Chippewa villages around the fur company post; surely they had heard the shots, too!

Ashman and Fairbanks, for it was they, explained that the Chippewas who were at war with the Sioux, had thought the shots had come from a Sioux raiding party, and they had been afraid.

What? Chippewas afraid of the Sioux? No—only afraid of Sioux horses. That is why the Chippewas always tried to fight in wooded or protected places. So, when the shots were heard, the Chippewas had refused to cross the lake to investigate, but had hastened to drive their cattle into the woods and prepare for a defensive battle.

Ashman and Fairbanks took the members of the expedition back with them immediately, promising that canoes would be sent across for the others.

*   *   *

The main body of the expedition joined them next day. No sooner had the Governor arrived than the Chippewas sent their oldest chief, Broken Arm, to talk to him.

The Governor, who was very tired, would have preferred to rest. But it would have been an affront to the Chippewas not to see him, and Governor Cass would not be guilty of this breach of diplomacy. To his surprise, however, Broken Arm came, bearing the pipe of peace, and dressed for council.

He greeted the Governor and his party with many elaborate gestures and much flowery talk. At the bidding of all the chiefs of his villages, he had come to request a council. Then, as soon as the Governor gave him permission to speak, Broken Arm cried out in his language

and all the lesser chiefs came and squatted behind him. Dufour acted as interpreter.

"Father," said Broken Arm to the Governor, "we are glad you have come among us, to see how we live. We are glad you have come to see what kind of country we inhabit, and to tell these things to our Great White Father, the President.

"Father, you see us here. We are poor. We need everything. We have neither knives nor blankets. We have no guns or powder. We have no lead or cloth. We have no kettles or tomahawks. We have no tobacco or whiskey. We hope you will give us these things.

"Father, we are glad that the Great White Father has thought proper to send you among us. We are glad to see his flag wave upon this lake. We are his children. He is our Father. We smoke the same pipe. We take hold of the same tomahawk. We are inseparable friends. It shall never be said that the Chippewa are ungrateful. Father, depend upon this, and take this pipe of peace as a pledge of our sincerity.

"Father, we are of the race of strong men. We are of the race of good warriors, and good hunters, but we cannot always kill game or catch fish. We can live a great while upon a little, but we cannot live upon nothing.

"Father, our wild rice is all eaten up. The buffalos live in the land of our enemies, the Sioux. We are hungry and naked. We are dry and needy. We hope you will relieve us.

"Father, the President is a very great man, even like a lofty pine upon the mountaintop. You also are a great man, and the Americans are a great people. Can it be possible they will allow us to suffer?"

Having spoken, he retreated and sat in the middle of the semi-circle of chiefs who had come with him. All the chiefs nodded in agreement and approval. It was true, as Henry could see, that these Chippewas were not nearly as well dressed as those of the Sault. Broken Arm's speech had been uttered in measured tones and with great dignity. He was not begging. He was asking the Great White Father not to let them starve. His plea was for his people, not for himself. Parks would call this begging; he would say that this was the way most of the Chippewas spoke. But this was not true. These Indians of Broken Arm's tribe were different from the proud warriors of Sassaba, and from those of the Grand Island Chippewas. Yet they all belonged to the same nation!

The Governor appeared to think over what he had heard. A murmur rose from among the women and the old men who came crowding behind their chiefs. But this stopped immediately when the Governor held up his hand for silence.

"Our Great White Father is a good man," said the

Governor. "He knows the troubles of his red children. But first, there are matters to make talk about. What is this war between the Chippewas and the Sioux?"

"Father, they attack us. They prevent us from hunting the buffalo," replied Broken Arm.

"Is it possible that the fault lies on both sides?" asked the Governor searchingly.

Broken Arm hesitated before answering. But at last, trying to be fair, he said, "It is possible."

"Will the Chippewas meet in council with the Sioux to put an end to the war?"

This was a proposal for which Broken Arm was not prepared. He took counsel with his other chiefs. There was a great whispering, and much flinging about of arms. But at last Broken Arm returned to face Governor Cass.

"We will take counsel with the Sioux under the flag of truce," he said.

"It is good," answered the Governor. "In the morning some of us will leave for the head of the Great Father of Waters. I will be among them. When we return, we hope you will have chosen men from among you to go with us to the Falls of St. Anthony to meet with the Sioux."

Then the Governor brought the council to an end by distributing to the old chieftain many of the things he had said his people needed.

*　　*　　*

That night, before he fell asleep, Henry lay thinking how far they had come from that day of setting out at

Detroit. So many things had happened to him that that day seemed already more than a year ago. Yet it was scarcely two months since they had left Detroit!

A year ago he had been at the mouth of the Mississippi. The mouth of the great river was so wide that it was almost indistinguishable from the waters of the gulf. He remembered the vast delta about which the river flowed, and now, in memory, he coursed back up the river as far as St. Louis. He remembered the great plantations, the Negro slaves working among the cotton rows right down to the river's edge, the levees, the river towns, the old plantation houses fronting upon the river, where barges, canoes, and ships of all kinds moved up and down without end.

Before his mind's eye the lower reaches of the Mississippi unfolded once again; he saw once more the broad, placid stream, brown with silt, flowing through the heart of the Continent. Truly, it was an artery dividing the United States, carrying on its commerce day and night over thousands of miles, that reached almost from its northern boundary to its southern coast.

Now, not far ahead, he was confident, lay his goal—the headwaters of this great river. It must be he who would find that source. This was what the Governor expected of him. He must not fail.

And, once he had done so, he could resume his studies of the Indians. He could return to the East—and to Jane.

Up the Mississippi

THE RIVER WHICH OPENED from Sandy Lake emptied into the Mississippi a mile from the fort. Early next morning three canoes carrying voyageurs and Chippewas, together with the Governor and Henry, swept into the larger river. The other members of the expedition had chosen to stay at the Sandy Lake fort until the Governor returned from the North.

At last Henry had reached the great Father of Waters. Now their course lay north. For some distance, the

country was not unknown. Other travelers had written
of it. Fur traders and Indians knew it. If they continued
to travel north, they would come to the land of the Assiniboin Indians. Traveling west, they would meet the
Sioux. All this time, they had traveled through the country of the Chippewas. They were now at the western
edge of that country, and close to the western boundary
of the Territory of Michigan.

At the place where they had entered the river, the Mississippi was sixty yards across. Its banks were crowded
by forests of elm, oak, maple, poplar, ash and pine. Wild
rice and bullrushes, with some willows growing among
them, separated the sandy shores from the forest. Could
this be the same river which flowed through the great
plantation country over a thousand miles to the south?
Henry wondered.

They were now going against the current. They had
been warned at the fort that the Mississippi, to the north,
was a river of many rapids. Yet none of them gave them
much trouble, for they were deep enough to permit travel
without portages.

The weather, for all that it was just past the middle of
July, was changing. The Governor was sensitive to it; he
felt it, as he said, "in his bones." Cloudy, rainy weather
prevailed, and gradually it grew colder. On the third day
out from Sandy Lake, they woke to find water frozen in

the bottom of the canoes. Though the ice was only as thick as a knife blade, Henry remembered what the Governor in Detroit had said about being caught in a cold season.

Soon the character of the land through which they moved changed completely. They left the region of forests for an upland prairie. The Mississippi wound like a serpent through a flat country covered with tall grass, wild rice, and rushes. Sometimes the grass grew so tall that they could not see above it when they sat in their canoes.

Henry noticed the change in the appearance of the country with growing excitement. All the things he had heard about from various travelers and Indians seemed now to be before his eyes. They could not be far from Leech Lake—and from the elusive La Biche. While the Governor sat stolidly in his canoe, seldom looking anywhere but ahead, Henry looked around in every direction, anxious to miss no sign, no clue to the source of the stream.

Ducks abounded here. Redwinged blackbirds clung to the reeds and rushes. Small white gulls rose in such great flocks that they often brushed the heads of the travelers as they went by. Their harsh screams echoed across the flat country. Now and then loons, blue herons, and wild geese rose from the water and flew away.

All that day and the next Henry studied the prairie

country. There was no change. Here and there little streams emptied into the greater, but there was nothing even remotely resembling a branch to the stream.

They had not been long on the journey next morning when they passed the mouth of a river entering on the left. The Governor called Henry's attention to it, though Henry had already noticed it.

"Do you know it, Schoolcraft? How well have you studied that birchbark map you copied?"

"Sir, by my calculations, that must be Leech River. Leech Lake is its source."

"Correct. Pike considers it the main source of the Mississippi."

"If so, what lies ahead?"

"Still other lakes. Will you go up Leech River?"

"No, sir. Not until I've satisfied myself as to what's before us."

"Well spoken. We shall see."

Henry had had only a few moments of doubt. It was true that the Mississippi seemed to narrow past the mouth of the Leech, but there was a considerable stream ahead still.

They pressed on.

*   *   *

Thirty-five miles above the mouth of the Leech River, they came to still another lake. This, Henry recognized as Little Lake Winnipec. It, too, had been on the birch-bark map.

Here they met two Chippewa women coming from the opposite direction. Henry signaled to Dufour that he would like to speak with them. Accordingly, the canoes turned toward them.

Henry expected the women to show some alarm, but they did not. They had been moving along the shore, pulling down and examining stalks of the wild rice. Seeing the party's canoes bearing down on them, they sat quietly waiting in their own light craft.

Dufour greeted them in their language and explained that one of the party wished to speak with them. He pointed to Henry.

"Which direction do you come from?" asked Henry.

They looked at each other as if they thought he could have seen as much. They motioned to the northwest.

"You travel all the way on this river?"

They nodded.

"Do you know where this river begins?"

They looked at each other, puzzled. Then one of them explained that they had only come down to inspect the wild rice, so that they might know when it would be ripe for the harvest. They had not come very far, only from the shore of Lake Winnibigoshish.

"Is there a Chippewa village there?"

"A small one of four lodges."

Henry thanked them and motioned the voyageurs to draw away.

Soon they entered Lake Winnibigoshish. This was the largest of the lakes they had seen since Sandy Lake. It seemed several times as large as that lake. Henry was confident that they were now close to the source of the Mississippi. This was one of the lakes on the birchbark map which had been sometimes called La Biche. Perhaps it was the source of the Mississippi. Henry begged the Governor to go to the lodges of the Chippewas so that he could speak with them.

The Chippewa village lay on the south shore of the lake. It was not, at first, in sight, but as they pushed farther out upon the lake from the bay out of which the Mississippi flowed, they saw the lodges.

The chief of the Chippewa village was Flat Mouth. He was delighted to see the Governor, though he had never before met him. Yet word of the Governor's great friendship for the Indians was widely spread over the Territory of Michigan and the country of the Chippewas.

The Governor introduced Henry, calling him "Destroyer of Rocks." He said Henry wished to make talk about the source of the Mississippi.

Flat Mouth immediately sent some of the braves around him to find the guides who belonged to the village. Then he brought out the pipe of peace.

When the guides assembled, there were quite a number

of them. Some were expert in the country south to Sandy
Lake. Still others knew best the area north to the country
of the Assiniboin. Three of them professed to know the
region to the west.

These three Henry singled out.

With Dufour at his side, he questioned them. Two
were young. One of these was called Red Hawk. The
other was known as Cloud-in-Eyes. The third was an
older man whose name was Yellow Head.

"I want to find the beginning of the Father of Waters,"
said Henry.

Both Red Hawk and Cloud-in-Eyes immediately
pointed into the west.

"A day's journey," added Cloud-in-Eyes.

When Henry turned to the older guide, Yellow Head
shook his head slowly.

"More," he said. "More days. There is a water blue as
the sky in the shape of an arrowhead. Manitou himself
has put it there. From the point of the arrowhead flows
the great Father of Waters."

Red Hawk and Cloud-in-Eyes immediately set up a
great clamor. Both of them talked at once. Dufour listened to each of them as well as he could, since both
talked rapidly, and with some heat. When they had finished, he turned doubtfully to Henry.

"They say the old one, he is crazy," he said. "The chief,
he nod, too. None has belief in him."

Henry hesitated but a moment. Then he said, "Say that we will take Red Hawk and Cloud-in-Eyes as guides. We will leave two of the Sandy Lake Chippewas here until our return."

With the new guides, they crossed the lake to the opening of a small stream to the west. This, the guides insisted, was the Father of Waters. But it was now evening, so, time to stop for the night.

However, Henry did not rest all that night. He was eager to reach the source of the river, to come at last to the goal of his long journey. His restlessness made him toss and turn most of the night. Once or twice he got up and walked out under the stars, where he stood in a night so chill that no insect bothered him.

How far they were now from the cities! How far from the sea! He stood deep in the heart of the Continent, where the springs of one of the greatest rivers in the world began. He did not know how many miles from the Gulf of Mexico he was now, but he knew that it must be over two thousand. Small wonder that he was excited!

He knew how few white men had come this way. Perhaps a fur-trader or two. Perhaps a voyageur. Zebulon Pike? Jonathan Carver? Neither had come this far. No other explorer had done so. Even Governor Cass had never before been so far out into the Territory he governed so well. To Henry belonged the thrill of discovery, and as he stood there under the stars, he was humbly grateful to Providence for having permitted him to come so far.

At four o'clock in the morning, they were on the way again. The river wound through the floor of a valley, a mile wide.

Then at last they came to another lake.

Here Red Hawk and Cloud-in-Eyes showed excitement, which communicated itself to Henry. The lake was a beautiful transparent body of water, and the guides touched its surface with the flat of their hands, calling out, "Cassina."

"That is the name of the lake," explained Dufour.

"Here! Here!" cried the guides together.

"Sometimes it is called Upper Red Cedar Lake," Dufour went on. "But it has now been name' Cassina in honor of the Governor."

"Here!" cried the guides again.

"What are they saying?" asked Henry.

"They say this lake is the beginning of the Mississippi."

They moved out upon the water.

"The lake, it is six miles wide and eight long," continued Dufour. "It is fed by two stream. One is call' the Turtle River. The other the French voyageur have call' the La Biche River."

La Biche! Once more Henry heard that name. His excitement increased.

"Ask them if this lake was ever so called."

Dufour did so. He listened to their replies and nodded. "They say it was."

So, then, this must indeed be the source of the Mississippi. At long last he had reached the goal he sought!

Henry was elated.

As the canoes made their way to the Chippewa village of ten lodges on a knoll of land on one shore of the lake, Henry was already deciding what he would write that night in his journal—

"To have visited both the source and the mouth of this celebrated stream, falls to the lot of few, and I believe there is no person living, beside myself, of whom this can be said. On the 10th of July, 1819, I passed out of the mouth of the Mississippi in a brig bound for New York, after descending it in a steamboat from St. Louis, and little thinking I should soon re-visit its waters; yet, on the 21st of July of the following year, I found myself seated in an Indian canoe, upon its source."

Tomorrow would begin the long trek home.

Yet, even as he composed these lines, something gnawed at him. It was the memory of those fugitive hints he had heard all the way from Detroit. The hints of that little jewel of a lake lost in the pines. Here at Cassina there were elms, maples, and some pines. But not many. Could this indeed be the lake meant by the tales he had listened to?

And, together with this doubt, there was another. Was old Yellow Head as crazy as Red Hawk and Cloud-in-Eyes had said he was?

But he did not speak of his doubts. The Governor, he saw, was now near to exhaustion. He could and would go no farther. Already he looked forward to the return journey with keen pleasure. So did Henry, for the memory of Jane Johnston pushed ever and again to the forefront of his thoughts, even now, in the moment of his triumph.

If Henry had wanted to press on, perhaps the Governor would have permitted him to do so. Governor Cass could have waited in the Chippewa village on Cassina Lake. But Henry was as anxious as the Governor to return.

And was this not, after all, the source of the great river? The guides should have known better than he or anyone else. Yet, it was true, Zebulon Pike had believed his guides in his own time. If only there had not been the disagreement in Flat Mouth's village!

So, thinking in this manner, thinking partly of Governor Cass and his well-being, thinking of Jane Johnston waiting at the Sault, Henry did not speak.

If only he had heeded his doubts!

The Blue Jewel

TWELVE YEARS LATER, Henry Schoolcraft was back on Cassina Lake.

This time his guide was an aging Chippewa. His name was Ozawindeb, which was the Chippewa for Yellow Head. This time there needed to be no other interpreter but Henry, for he had learned to speak the Chippewa language, and Jane Johnston had helped to teach him.

In those twelve years much had happened to Henry. He had gone back to the Sault de Ste. Marie in 1822, as the Indian agent for that post. He had married Jane John-

ston, who had so attracted him when first he had visited
there. He had studied all he could find to learn about the
Chippewas and other Indians. Jane had been his untiring
helper. He had written a book about Indian legends and
lore. He met often now with many Indian tribes. He had
come to know the country of the Territory of Michigan
as well as the voyageurs, even as well as many of the
Indians.

But all the time, he continued to hear tales of the source
of the Father of Waters. Again and again, there was talk
of a "little jewel of blue water." Always it was deep in
the forest, surrounded by pines. Then, when he was sent
to meet in council with the Chippewa and the Sioux on
the St. Croix and Chippewa Rivers, once again he heard
of this blue water from an old Indian.

And there he heard that it was shaped like an arrowhead.

Then it was that he remembered Yellow Head, the
Chippewa they had said was crazy, the guide he himself
had rejected. He remembered all his doubts about Cassina Lake, and how he had not spoken of them.

He wrote to the War Department, and told them that
he now believed he had not, after all, found the true
source of the Father of Waters that July day in 1820.
The War Department ordered him to find the headwaters
of that great river, and to map them now so that no mistake could ever again be made.

When Henry came to Flat Mouth's village and sought out Yellow Head, he was afraid that Yellow Head might have died. But he was still alive and he came before Henry, looking little changed. He had been old before, and he was still so, now.

"Do you remember me, Yellow Head?" Henry asked.

The old man nodded. "You are the Destroyer of Rocks. You came with Big Belly many, many moons ago. You listened to those who did not believe me."

"Perhaps I was wrong, Yellow Head."

"You were wrong, Paw-gwa-be-can-e-ga."

There was no trace of grievance in his voice. He did not hold Henry's mistake against him.

"I have come back to be right this time, Yellow Head. Will you show me now where the Father of Waters takes its source?"

"I am an old man, Paw-gwa-be-can-e-ga. I have waited many years to be proved right. I will go gladly."

So he had gone as their guide. He was eager to prove to his red brothers, however late in his life it might be, that he had always spoken the truth of this, that it was Red Hawk and Cloud-in-Eyes who had been wrong.

There were sixteen of them in all, traveling in five light canoes.

This time they did not pause on Cassina Lake, as they had done before. They pressed on across the lake. Henry remembered with regret his easy acceptance of what his guides had told him. If only he had voiced his doubts on that day, now, so long ago!

Yellow Head led them straight to the mouth of the river the voyageurs had named La Biche. They pushed up this swift stream. Their light canoes fairly danced on the water.

Thirty miles from Cassina Lake, they came to another lake.

Yellow Head grinned and said, "La Biche."

"La Biche again!" cried Henry. "How many are there?"

"The fur traders call many lakes by this name. They find lake, they get lost. They find another lake, they think it the same. They call each of them La Biche. They travel around in circles. There is La Biche here. There is La Biche in other place. The La Biche River is the Father of Waters."

"Is there a Chippewa name for this lake, Yellow Head?"

"We call it Bemidji."

"Then this is the La Biche which is the source of the Mississippi?"

Yellow Head shook his head. "Not yet. Two days from this lake. Then the long portage."

"How long?"

"Thirteen pauses, as the voyageur measures it. Then we will be there."

They went on through Lake Bemidji. Now they trav-

eled not west but south. Henry was puzzled, but Yellow
Head seemed so serenely sure of where he was leading
him that he did not question him. Red Hawk and Cloud-
in-Eyes had seemed sure, too. Yet they had been wrong.
But Yellow Head was so perfectly calm that Henry did
not dare to doubt him.

They came to the mouth of another river.

"Father of Waters," said Yellow Head. "Now we go
up, for two days. Then we walk a long time."

The Mississippi here was a small, narrowing stream. It
bore the appearance of a river close to its source. Trees
grew almost into the water, which was fine and clear, so
that the bottom shone through the water.

For two days they went on up the river. Then it grew
too narrow for canoes. It became a mountain torrent, narrow and rocky, filled with foamy water rushing through
a country where few men had ever walked.

They began the long portage.

Slowly, mile upon mile, they moved into the southwest
through the forest along a trail that was scarcely marked,
for it was traveled very little and known only to the Chippewas. For a long time they walked through low country,
but at last they came to a region of hills.

The portage led them to the highest ridge. When Yellow Head came to the top of this ridge, he stood aside to
wait for Henry.

Henry found him pointing down. "You have waited

many years for this, Paw-gwa-be-can-e-ga," he said softly.

There, shining like a jewel in its setting of pines, was a lake in the shape of an arrowhead. A deep neck of land that was a large island came down into the lake from the far end. From the point of the lake below flowed the stream that they had been following.

Here at last was the true source of the Mississippi.

Once again Henry felt both humble and triumphant. This time he knew no doubts to temper his joy and gratitude.

"What is it called, Yellow Head?"

"The Chippewas call it Omushkos. To the voyageurs it is another La Biche."

Henry turned to William Boutwell, another member of the party who had come to stand at his side. "You are the scholar, Boutwell. Can you think of a classical word which could indicate the head or true source of a river?"

"How about the Latin, Mr. Schoolcraft? *Verum Caput* —the true head—or the nouns, *veritas caput?*"

Henry pondered for a moment. Then he shook his head. "No. I have it. We shall take the last two syllables of *veritas* and the first of *caput*. We shall call it Itasca. Come, let us go down to it."

They descended to the lake, where they put their canoes into its blue water and pushed across to the tip of the island to make camp.

Afterward, when they had rested, Henry had the men

cut down some trees at the head of the island. Then he had a flagpole fashioned and a flag fixed to it. The pole was dug deep into the ground and braced with forked sticks.

From the wood the men had cut down, most of them cut sticks they could shape into canes, so that they would always remember the shining lake in the dense woods, the blue water surrounded by hills and the tall forest.

That night, by the light of the campfire, Henry completed his map, with the wise help of old Yellow Head. The two of them sat long by the fire, long after the rest of the party had fallen asleep. They spoke of many things, of the beauty and solitude of the wilderness, of the hidden waters in the land of the Chippewas, of Henry's success at last in reaching the goal set for him by Governor Cass twelve years before.

How long it had taken him!

"But all things in life that are good are worth the struggle, Paw-gwa-be-can-e-ga," said Yellow Head gravely.

*   *   *

On the way back next day, Henry paused long on the ridge to gaze down upon the lake he had named Itasca.

It lay below, blue as the sky, nestling in the hills, locked in by the forest. The Father of Waters was but a trickling stream which flowed out of it to become the great Mississippi, to empty thousands of miles away into the Gulf

of Mexico. The American flag flew high on the pole on the island where they had left it, red and white and blue against the deep green forest and the cobalt water of the lake.

He had been within days of this place twelve years before, but he had been too impetuous to listen to a wise Indian who knew where it was.

Now he had found it.

He turned from it at last. He was more humble than he was proud.

The last of it that he saw shone like a blue jewel among the trees, the bluest of all the lakes and rivers in this land of sky-blue waters.